HEALING THE
SICK MIND

HEALING THE
SICK MIND

By
Dr. Harry Guntrip

Foreword by
Dr. Henry V. Dicks

616.8916
G95.9

2-7-96

X
G755

APPLETON-CENTURY
AFFILIATE OF
MEREDITH PRESS

ACKNOWLEDGMENTS

It is a great pleasure to express my warm thanks to Dr. H. V. Dicks for his kindness in writing a Foreword. It was he who, as First Nuffield Professor of Psychiatry in Leeds, drew me in 1946 deep into psychotherapy, first introduced me to the work of Dr. Fairbairn, and provided clinical research facilities for me in the Leeds University Department of Psychiatry. His own personal emphasis on primary fear and dependence as lying behind all the neuroses (Cp. *Clinical Studies in Psychopathology*, 1939, Edward Arnold Ltd.) not only gave him a sympathetic attitude to Fairbairn's revision of theory, but was also an early influence on my thinking.

I wish also to thank Dr. J. D. Sutherland (Medical Director, Tavistock Clinic, London) and Dr. R. E. D. Markillie (Leeds University Dept. of Psychiatry) for valuable criticisms of the manuscript, and Dr. R. Laing for criticisms of chapter 11. Finally, my best thanks are due to my wife, not only for her help in preparing the manuscript but also for her understanding encouragement of my work.

Ghirlandaio's *Old Man and Grandchild* expresses the relationship of complete trust between child and adult, which is the basis of mental health.

FOREWORD

BY HENRY V. DICKS

It is a pleasure to be asked by Dr. Guntrip to write a foreword to this, his latest book, which is intended to acquaint the wider public with his views of the essential task and significance of psychotherapy as a contribution to man's endeavour to understand and master his secret fear and hate of life. This endeavour the author rightly refers to as Priority No. 1. But while couched in deceptively simple language, this volume offers much to those professionally concerned with problems of human adaptation to self and others. Dr. Guntrip may be called an idealist by some who read this book, a man who must hunt out every trace of weakness and suffering from the dark corners of the personality. This, I think, would be to misunderstand the intention of his book. For all his human concern and sympathy, Guntrip is also a searcher after adequate concepts and theories to account for *all* the phenomena he meets in the clinic or the consulting room. And, like others among present-day exponents of the psychodynamic viewpoint, he has tried to get beyond the point at which Freud stopped. The cultural climate, profoundly changed by world events as well as by the impact of Freud's genius on our epoch, has thrown up new problems of mental sickness—especially those of frightening detachment—a sense of depression more akin to deep insecurity, helplessness and futility. Dr. Guntrip tries, I think most interestingly and constructively, to interpret and give meaning to the origins of this subtler, more elusive malaise which was only hinted at in the original Freudian scheme, though capable of being developed from it. In other words, he is seeking a new theoretical model for psychiatry. I myself have attempted to ask the question what lay behind and motivated the various manifestations of disordered sexuality, hysteria and obsessive-compulsive behaviour and defied attempts at cure. Like Dr. Guntrip, I saw my hypothetical answer not in unalterable 'physical' genetics, but in the all-pervasiveness of infantile fear and insecurity. In 1939 I already wrote, summarizing my views of 'first causes':

'. . . . every patient with mental illness was more afraid
than he could tolerate when he was a baby, and the faults
in his psychic structure represent the gallant attempts to
allay this intolerable feeling by the inadequate means at
his disposal.'*

Dr. Guntrip's book is a reasoned and clinically supported
development of this sentence, and it makes a fresh contribution
to medical psychology. While I would hope that he may have
received some encouragement to explore this thesis during the
years when he was my valued colleague at Leeds, I know that
he has arrived at similar conclusions by his own path and on
the basis of rich experience. His long collaboration in a clinical
department of a medical school entitles him also to criticize,
as he does with good effect, the essentially shallow and mechanistic ideas which are being propounded at the present time
by a section of our profession, who claim to be more 'scientific'
than the approach of psychoanalysts and cognate systems, but
miss nearly everything that makes us human rather than
laboratory rats!

I will leave the reader to judge where greater depth and
promise lies, in the confidence that this present volume will
greatly help many people to understand the inwardness of the
psychotherapeutic process, and the underlying concepts with
which a mature and humane therapist goes to work.

London, W.1.

---

* *Clinical Studies in Psychopathology*, London, Arnold, 1939, p. 234.

CONTENTS

CONTENTS

INTRODUCTION

This book is a sequel to an earlier book, *You and Your Nerves*, which grew out of a series of ten broadcast talks given in the 'Silver Lining' feature of the BBC Light Programme in 1950. The talks were published in a somewhat expanded form in 1951, in response to some 1,500 letters which showed how great was the need for both enlightenment and practical help in this matter of neurosis. The publication of the book caused a further inflow of letters during the ensuing years, which all showed how widespread this need continues to be. The demand for knowledge in this field becomes more insistent as the gravity of the problem of 'mental health' is coming to be appreciated. *You and Your Nerves* was designed to provide a simple, non-technical account of this illness which might serve as both a guide and to some extent as a support for those who are so afflicted.

The aim of this present book is different. In asking me to prepare a second edition of *You and Your Nerves*, Allen and Unwin kindly suggested that I might wish to expand it now into a larger book. On the whole, however, it seems better to let it stand in its original form, and to carry the whole enquiry further in a new volume. The psychological study of human personality has not stood still in the last twelve years, and there are newer views to take into account. But what is equally important, the whole subject has been brought before the public in a new and more urgent way. We have had a 'Mental Health Year', and radio and TV broadcasts on the subject have created a much wider understanding of the serious nature of the problem. Popular magazine articles, Press correspondence such as that in the *Guardian* in 1960, and the BBC Reith Lectures by Professor Carstairs, have all helped to awaken the mind of the community. It is slowly coming to be recognized that the problem of Mental Health is far greater and more complicated, both as to its causes and treatments, than has ever before been understood in the history of the human race. In fact, 'Mental Health' in the sense in which we are now using this term is a distinctly new concept. In 1950 Dr. H. V. Dicks wrote:

'I think of our work as something new and comparable to the invention of "new means of conquest of another dimension" . . . though I should like a better name than that of "mental health".

I believe what we do is a new kind of thing which has never been done before on the basis of rationally intelligible generalized concepts won in the empirical way through the exercise of a variety of technical skills. I believe that "mental health" is an emerging goal and a value for humanity of a kind comparable to the notions of "finding God", "salvation", "perfection" or "progress" which have inspired various eras of our history, as master values which at the same time implied a way of life.'*

I have designed this book for those among the reading public who have become aware of, and are concerned about, this grave problem, an aim which goes beyond the purpose of the earlier volume of giving practical help to actual sufferers.

You and Your Nerves will, I hope, retain its usefulness for the original purpose. It gives a non-technical account of the simplest and most easily recognizable facts about mental illness; the symptoms and emotional tensions and conflicts of which the nervously ill person is pretty generally consciously aware, even though unconscious factors are involved. It is widely understood today that unmanageable sexual and aggressive impulses are neurotic symptoms, and most people know what is meant by an 'anxiety state'. Hoardings and popular songs combine to warn us against 'tension' and urge us to 'relax' with the help of some particular type of bed-mattress, or some special brand of cigarettes, or a particularly soothing drink as a night-cap. *You and Your Nerves* gives what we may call the 'Classic Diagnosis' in terms of impulse-management, guilt and depression, but this indicates that there is now much more to be said. In particular 'treatment' was only very sketchily dealt with in one chapter, and the widespread discussion of the nature and adequacy of psychotherapy in recent years makes it necessary to go much more fully into this matter.

Furthermore, the investigation of neurosis has come to probe into much deeper levels of our mental make-up than were taken into account in the study of Depression. These were touched on in *You and Your Nerves* at several points where 'schizoid problems' were mentioned. These concern the ravages of the most elementary fears lying behind problems of sex, aggression and guilt, the fears which are responsible for the obstruction of the initial growth of a basically strong personality. This calls now for much fuller treatment. In terms of what I called the 'Classic Diagnosis', neurosis may be described as the conflicts that rage in us, in their most important part unconsciously, between fear, anger (aggression),

* *Brit. J. Med. Psychol.* Vol. 23, p. 3. Address from the Chair to the Medical Section of the British Psychological Society.

guilty feelings and the need for love (which may turn sex into an obsession), resulting in a persisting state of general anxiety with physical disturbances, and even the crippling emotional deadlock known as Depression. This kind of diagnosis, based on the facts of the struggle that obviously goes on against 'bad' or antisocial impulses of sex and aggression, the 'lusts and passions of the flesh', is a scientific version of the centuries old 'Moral Psychology' which was Freud's starting-point.

Unfortunately this account of the matter does not explain why it is that human beings have antisocial impulses. The traditional view, accepted by Freud, was that they were simply innate, part of our biological make-up. This view is no longer adequate and we must go deeper than the level of 'moral conflicts' to the fears which arise in the human infant before he is sufficiently developed for morality to have any meaning. Here we are at *the very beginnings of the formation of personality,* and what happens for good or ill at that stage forms today the major research problem in this field. Thus, after discussing 'The Classic Diagnosis' in Part 1 of this present book, I have in Part 2 sought to show in what 'The Deeper Understanding' consists. Part 3 then surveys in a fuller way than was possible in *You and Your Nerves* the complex and many-sided problems of 'Treatment'. I have not felt it necessary in this book to preserve the direct, simple and conversational style of the original broadcast talks, since our purpose here is a closer discussion of the whole subject of 'Mental Health', even if it be in small compass.

It should be stated definitely that the term 'Nerves' represents a completely out of date approach to the problem. It is a relic of the time when medical science, as distinct from the old 'family doctor', had little use for the mental personality as such, and took it for granted that the causes of all ills must be in the body, as indeed some still assume. The more technical medical counterpart of the popular 'nerves' was the term 'neurasthenia' (weak nerves) which has today died out of the medical vocabulary. Yet the term 'neurasthenia', if its exclusive reference to the body is set aside, stated a truth that was lost sight of in the earlier researches into the problems of the mental personality. All the stress was laid by Freud on difficulties over controlling and civilizing our 'strength', managing our powerful antisocial instincts. It now, however, becomes ever more apparent that mental illness arises out of our struggles to defend ourselves against our 'weakness' as separate individuals facing the overwhelming pressures of a baffling complex environment, after we have been first undermined by a disturbed childhood.

Freud began by taking over uncritically the traditional age-old belief that 'Instincts versus Social Controls' was the fundamental problem of human living. This view, older than St Paul and Plato, emerged in Freudian scientific dress in the theory of the 'ego' (our ordinary conscious self) and the 'super-ego' (conscience) battling against the 'id' or 'it', our supposedly impersonal biological drives. This view, however, enabled Freud to open up this field of research, and steadily, and at first under Freud's own pioneer leading, emphasis has shifted off the control of instincts and on to the problem of laying the foundations in infancy of a whole, united, non-anxious, self-confident and active personality, in the medium of good parent-child relationships. We are coming to understand what grave damage can be done to personality development in the earliest years of life, and are coming to be more concerned about 'primary fears' and resulting 'ego-weakness' than about 'powerful instincts' as the cause of mental ill-health in the adult. This is, to parody the old term, not 'neurasthenia' but 'ego-asthenia', not 'weak nerves' but an 'undermined personality' dating from the earliest years. This view now sets psychotherapy its stiffest task, to find out how to promote basic regrowth of inner strength in a person who has been anxiety-ridden for a lifetime.

This point of view is of more recent development. I have given a detailed account of its emergence in theory, in *Personality Structure and Human Interaction.** A more general account of the matter is given here. Turning from theory to clinical practice, it must be noted that resources of recent years have expanded under the National Health Service in the form of far more numerous Out-Patient Clinics, but the fact has to be faced that at present this does more to reveal the size of the problem than to provide an answer to it. Provided the General Practitioner is a sympathetic man who has been at some special pains to understand the needs of 'nervous patients' and can find time to 'listen', the patient is often far more helped by the G.P. than by the pyschiatric clinic where, after a long wait, he may be seen for 15 minutes, given a prescription for pills and told to come again in a month. Under the pressure of far too many cases nothing more can be done, and in these circumstances the psychiatrist knows far less about the patient than the G.P. does. One of the most important pieces of work developing today is that pioneered by Dr. Michael Balint in training G.P.s in the psychodynamic approach to their patient's illnesses.

But even the G.P., under modern conditions, has far less time

* In the International Psychoanalytical Library, London, Hogarth Press, 1961.

to 'listen' and is apt to know much less of his patients as persons than did the old family doctor. Whatever the values and advantages of the highly organized 'business' of modern state medicine, it is very definitely a bad setting, and altogether too impersonal, for the treatment of the incipiently nervously or emotionally ill. There is still the prevailing tendency to use the diagnostic label of 'hysterical reaction' as a term of veiled or implied criticism, and to add to it the prescription of a tranquillizer. It must be emphatically stated that this is not an adequate attempt to deal with mental ill-health. I do not believe anyone thinks it is, but there is the danger of thinking that to do something is better than to do nothing, and then to pass on to the complacent assumption that we really are doing something, which turns out in practice to be far from satisfactory.

The best safeguard against complacency, however, is probably the dissatisfaction of the mentally ill themselves who know that the help they get is for the most part far from solving their problems. There is some critical public discussion about psychotherapy as to whether it does or does not produce quick or indeed any results. There are reactions against it in some medical and psychological circles, in favour of drug and other treatments. Yet in truth there is even more dissatisfaction expressed with the results of drugs by those who have to take them. The danger is that in such a situation realities may be obscured by partisanship, controversy and prejudice. The realities of this problem are concerned with assessing precisely in just what conditions drugs, psychotherapy or any other form of treatment should be resorted to, and what kind of results are to be expected. We should not waste time pitting one kind of treatment against another.

So far as one can judge the present position is roughly this: no conceivable psychiatric drug can possibly turn an undermined human being into a maturely developed person, but it can, rightly prescribed, do a lot to control tensions, reduce symptoms, and make life more bearable. On the other hand, psychotherapy, which aims to promote the development of the personality out of a fear-ridden and anxiety-burdened state into stable maturity, has not yet been able to produce the results we would wish for, though it is not true that it does not produce any results. It is still, particularly in psychoanalytical researches, seeking to probe to the bottom of the nature of the problem. Along both the medical-physical and the psychotherapeutic lines knowledge and results are at present partial and we have much more to learn. Professor Dennis Hill writes, 'We are not quite sure what we are doing. A new empiricism seems to have evolved in psychiatry, in which the aim is the cure of the symptoms, rather than the development of understanding of the illnesses which give rise to them, which should lead ultimately to the control and prevention of those illnesses.'*

We may therefore say that *the problem of 'Healing the Sick Mind' is our number one priority.* I quote a report in *The Yorkshire Post* of Dec. 28, 1961:

> 'As universities and colleges expand, mental illhealth among students increases. Research at the Universities of Leeds and London indicates that 15·9 per cent of any group of students following a course of higher education will show symptoms of mental illhealth.'

Dr. Ronald Still, Senior Medical Officer of Health at the University of Leeds, made a survey of the years 1949-1960 which showed that

> 'of the 11,605 men and women students who consulted a university doctor during this period, 15·9 per cent showed psychological symptoms of all degrees of severity. . . . A classification of the total of 1,843 cases of mental disturbance shows that the largest group—134—concerned acute situational maladjustment. Twenty-three cases concerned sexual deviations, 13 acute schizophrenia, 77 neurotic depressive reactions and 127 disturbances of sleep.'

The conference at which these figures were given naturally sought for explanations:

> 'Dr. Nicholas Malleson, head of the research unit on student problems at the University of London Institute of Education, suggests that it is because student life demands a continuously high standard of intellectual efficiency that the incidence of those attending for psychological help is high. Contributory causes of mental ill-health among students are believed to be examination tension, lack of adequate study facilities and an inability to make the transition from Sixth Form to University adequately.'

Such an analysis of causes as this is most unconvincing. I do not believe that reasonably stable young people coming from normally happy and secure homes will break down in face of no greater

* *Burden on the Community: The Epidemiology of Mental Illness.*

difficulties than these. Those who do so break down, will do so because their mental health has already been undermined before ever they reach the University, and the search for causes must go deeper.

What of the remedies? The report I am quoting stated that:

'Possible remedial factors suggested were the provision of more halls of residence, more and smaller tutorial groups, a more adequate system of introduction to the university environment, a regularization of the examination system, and a more acute recognition by university teachers of their pastoral responsibility for students.'

All these things are, of course, good. They correspond to what I have called in Chapter 9 treatment by alleviation of environmental pressures and increase of supports. There is little else that can be done for students by universities, which only shows that far more radical thinking needs to be done on the problems of prevention rather than cure.

In further justification of the claim that Mental Health is the top priority in research, I quote from 'An Address from the Chair to the Medical Section of the British Psychological Society' on Jan. 23, 1952, by Dr. J. D. Sutherland, Medical Director of the Tavistock Clinic, London. He said:

'A little reflexion on the scale and cost of psychological illness is salutary.'

One of his reflexions was as follows:

'Russell Fraser (1947) and his colleagues showed that approximately 10 per cent of the industrial population had suffered from definite and disabling neurotic difficulties, and a further 20 per cent from minor forms of neurosis, during the course of six months. . . . Neurotic illness caused between a quarter and a third of all absence from work due to illness; neurosis causes more absence than colds and influenza.'*

Evidently the pressures of 'demands . . . for a continuously high standard of efficiency' are not confined to university students. Yet it can hardly be claimed that the pressures on students and industrial workers are greater than those put upon young mothers with two or more children, seven and not five days a

* *Brit. J. Med. Psychol.* Vol. xxv, Pts. 2 and 3, 1952, p. 71.

week. If breakdowns under the pressures of life are so widespread, the proper inference is that we are bringing up far too many children who have become seriously emotionally disturbed long before they have to face the demands that await them in the late teens and in adult life.

PART 1

THE CLASSIC DIAGNOSIS OF
MENTAL ILL-HEALTH

CHAPTER ONE

THE MEANING OF MENTAL HEALTH

As we have noted in the introduction, the idea of 'mental health' is in process of acquiring a new significance today. Dr. Dicks suggests that it is a new 'value' for us, but he did not altogether like the term. That feeling is shared by many. As compared with the religious concept of 'salvation' or the secular concept of 'progress', the idea of 'mental health' does not make any very sharp or challenging impact, and different people mean very different things by it; though that is just as true of the ideas of salvation or progress. These ideas are to a considerable extent defined by reference to their opposites. Religiously, mankind was conceived as born in sin and shapen in iniquity, and salvation meant liberation from this condition. Politically and economically, countries like China and Japan seemed to have stagnated for centuries in an unchanging social order, and in Europe France and Russia perpetuated a feudal way of life, until at last the impact of modern science, and the revolutionary changes in both modes of living and ways of thinking that it stimulated, set going vast social upheavals out of which the idea of 'progress' was born.

In the same way, the idea of 'mental health' is inevitably closely linked with its opposite, that of 'mental ill-health', in its extreme forms known as psychosis and in its more common forms as psychoneurosis, or popularly 'nerves'. Mental health and mental ill-health must be defined with reference to each other, and yet neither of them is easy to conceptualize in a clear-cut and generally acceptable way. It is easier to feel the vigorous but friendly impact of the mentally healthy person or the sense of strain and tension in the anxious sufferer from neurosis, than to say in a word exactly what constitutes their nature and difference. The definition of mental ill-health is to some extent complicated by moral issues, for what today we call neurosis, is still widely regarded as selfishness and was at one time even treated as devil-possession. Experts are by no means quite clear as to how the notion of 'illness', fixed in its broad meaning by long association with physical disease, can be applied to disturbances of the mental personality.

Even so, it is usually easier to describe, if not to define, a negative concept like mental ill-health than a positive one such as mental health. As, for example, with a concept like 'world peace', we may easily find ourselves talking in large vague ways that do not get down to earth very successfully. Thus, instead of attempting to begin with definitions, it may well be better to plunge into the investigation and allow total impressions to grow in our minds as to what it is all about. At least we all know the difference between the person who is *inwardly free* to get on happily and constructively with real aims and interests while finding it easy to mix and work with his fellows, and the person whose whole approach to life is *obstructed from within* by chronic lack of self-confidence, timidity and irritability in dealing with other people, and vague but persisting physical disturbance, so that he never feels well and never happy. We know that all too many people fall into the second group, and for the first time in history in this century a tremendous concentration of world-wide concern and research has developed around this fact.

The ancient Romans had a much-quoted saying, *Mens sana in corpore sano*, freely translated as 'a sane (or sound) mind in a sound body'. In our time, medical science has made, and is still making, enormous strides towards the conquest of physical disease. Whether this of itself is sufficient to enable us all to have 'a sound body' is by no means proved. Certainly we live much longer on average than our forbears did. The extraordinary advances of modern surgery and new drug discoveries (such as the antibiotics) have meant that many illnesses which used to be fatal or crippling can now be cured. The equally important if less exciting and romantic advances in sanitation and public health measures have gone far to eliminating the plagues that used to decimate the earth. The medical supervision of children has ensured that countless numbers get a far better start in life than they would have had a hundred years ago, or even fifty.

Nevertheless, in spite of all this improvement, we are faced with a double threat, on the one hand from what are often called 'the diseases of civilization' of which we may cite cancer as an example, and on the other hand from the insidious 'psychosomatic diseases' which come much closer to the subject of this book. Allowing for the differences made in the past by the ravages of ignorance, lack of hygienic and sanitary conditions, the prevalence of plagues and infections against which there was then no defence, all of which scientific knowledge can today combat so much more successfully, it may well be true that the individual of a hundred or two hundred years ago who escaped those dangers and lived to a hardy old age, was fitter and sounder in body than most moderns who never walk if they can ride, ride a car and not a horse, and live at a pace and under a pressure unknown to earlier generations. Probably the far greater number who today live to be eighty are not as bodily strong and healthy as were the smaller number of octogenarians in the past. Nothing is really proved by citing individual cases, but it is of interest to note that Sidney Barnes, the greatest bowler ever produced by English cricket, was at the age of ninety still working as a clerk for the Staffordshire County Council.

Evidence, however, of a more convincing and broadly based kind may be cited from *The Hambledon Men* by E. V. Lucas. This is an account of the most famous cricketers between the years 1750 and 1850. Lucas quotes from Mr. Haygarth, a writer of that period, forty-four short biographies of the leading players. Two died in their thirties. Practically all of them lived into their sixties. 50 per cent or 22 lived into their seventies. 20 per cent or nine lived into their eighties, and two lived into their nineties. Nor did this amount to a lingering senility. William Beldham, the greatest batsman of his day, played in great matches for thirty-five years. At eighty-six he walked seven miles to watch an England match. At ninety-two he was visited by Mr. Haygarth who found him working in his garden before 8 a.m. He died aged ninety-six. William Fennex, a famous all-rounder, completed forty seasons in first-class games and was still bowling well in practice in his sixties. At seventy-five he walked ninety miles in three days carrying an umbrella, a bundle of clothes and three cricket bats, and spent only three shillings. John Small Senr., the greatest batsman prior to Beldham, started in county matches at the age of eighteen and his last first-class match, for Hampshire *v.* M.C.C. at Lord's, was in 1798 when he was sixty-one. He played thus for forty-three seasons. He was a gamekeeper till he was seventy, beginning his day with a seven mile tour on foot, and he followed the hounds on foot at eighty-five. He played the tenor violin without the aid of spectacles till the last year of his life, dying at the age of eighty-nine. Squire E. H. Budd played for fifty years and died over seventy-five years of age.

These remarkable facts concerning men who lived without any

of the advantages of modern medical science, but who also lived relatively simple, natural, outdoor lives, give serious grounds for thinking that, in our own time, what medical science gives on the one hand, our modern way of living takes away on the other. It seems to be a distinct possibility that the 'advances' of medical science are in danger of being counterbalanced by the 'advances' in civilization, so far as bodily health is concerned. It is clear that a sound body cannot be produced and preserved solely by physical medicine. It rests on our whole mode of living so far as 'civiliza-tion' is concerned, and this is even more the case when we turn from the problems of 'a sound body' to those of 'a sound mind'. Here the benefits of modern civilization are even more dubious, and the psychosomatic diseases warn us of the extent to which health of body and of mind go together. We shall have reason later to look more closely into this. Meanwhile it will suffice to say that the advances of psychological and psychiatric science have produced very uncertain and inadequate results so far as anything worth calling 'radical cure' of mental illness is concerned.

In the *British Medical Journal* for April 2, 1960, a correspondent wrote in reply to a critic of psychotherapy: 'One would like to enquire whether this writer has had any personal experience of treating psychoneurotics by the orthodox methods commonly em-ployed in all progressive mental hospitals. I had over twenty-five years of such experience, but found as many others have found, that they afforded temporary palliation only for the psychoneurotic' (p. 1051). It is not too much to say that advances in 'mental science' have so far served mainly to reveal the alarming extent and nature of mental illness, and to show how deep-seated and stubborn a thing it is to 'cure'. I do not think anyone would dispute the view that what we must aim at ultimately, in dealing with mental ill-health, is prevention rather than cure. Mental illness is so vast a problem, when all its varied forms are taken into account, that were our resources in psychiatry and psycho-therapy far greater than they are, it would still be quite impos-sible to eliminate neurosis by attempting to cure individuals. At present, those who get any considerable amount of individual help are the lucky few.

Professor Eysenck, who is not an advocate of psychotherapy, states the proportions of the problem. He writes:

'The incidence of mental disorders in modern life is truly frightening. Few people quite realize the implications of recent trends. Approximately half of all hospital beds in Great Britain and the United States are given over to patients suffering from mental disorders. One person in 35 will be certified mentally ill some time during his life. . . . About a quarter (some put it as high as 50 per cent) of those who visit their G.P. for ostensibly physical ailments are found to suffer completely or mainly from mental illnesses. No wonder that the problem of cure and alleviation of these mental disorders occupies a prominent place in modern medical practice.'*

These figures quoted by Eysenck are those generally accepted. Our fear-ridden world is creating disturbed personalities faster than any direct remedial activities, medical, psychotherapeutic and social, can cope with them. It would need not so much a political and social, as a cultural revolution, to create a world in which parents could be non-anxious and little children be brought up without fear. We have not as yet made advances towards 'a sound mind' which are in any way comparable with those made towards 'a sound body', and this latter goal cannot be fully attained without the former. In this matter modern civilization, or the use human beings are making of it, seems to be proving an even greater menace to mental than to physical health. We have discovered the vitamins needed for bodily health, but, judging by the prevalence not only of neurosis but of crime, and adolescent and teenage crime at that, our civilization is sadly lacking in the emotional vitamins of personality growth. Dr. Conrad Lorenz, in a lecture at Leeds University, told of a puppy brought up in total isolation form birth. It simply lay inert and lifeless. That this was not due to lack of stimulation to activity but to the inhibiting effects of a state of total fear was proved by the fact that when it was given a tranquillizer to calm its fear, it began to romp about like any normal puppy. The total failure of its environment to nourish it psychologically led to a state of total paralysing fear. Such an experiment shows that the environment of the new-born is psychologically so utterly important, that mental illness is in truth what Dr. Winnicott calls 'an environmental deficiency disease.'†

If one of the physical 'diseases of civilization' is cancer, we must add that the psychosomatic diseases, all having their psychological origins in emotional tension in the mental personality, also have their roots in our way of living. They are fed by the pace and strain and tension of modern life on all hands, linked as these are with false values. The things aimed at in search of life, bring death. So true is this that, as we have already said,

* *The Uses and Abuses of Psychology*, Pelican, 1953.
† *Collected Papers*, London, Tavistock Publications, p. 162.

purely medical science cannot ultimately eradicate all physical illness so long as human beings are subjugated to such intense pressures of anxiety and fear. The social security given by the welfare state on the one hand is taken away on the other by the remorseless pressure and drive of economic competition, and of international competition and rivalry, both economic and military. This affects each single individual, both through his daily work and through the Press, Radio and TV, to a far greater extent than was true a century ago, when it was possible for ordinary citizens to be relatively unaffected by a war if it did not happen to be fought over their bit of countryside. Furthermore, we do not now talk much about crimes due to poverty, but crime due to the affluent society, and in so far as economic prosperity comes to men and women ill-equipped to use it for constructive living, they seem to be only able to fight to get more and more of what they cannot use.

The problem, however, is not therefore hopeless. There is a vicious circle involved. The more mentally disturbed the individual is, the less well he stands up to the strains of modern life, and the more he is broken down by them the more disturbed he becomes. Something is still to be done by enabling the individual, first to withstand the pressure of our present-day world, and then to work for its essential betterment in matters relating to mental health. We need to create a civilization which is 'mental health conscious', rather than money conscious or power conscious or success conscious or status conscious. Mental health is our first priority, since without it no other advances or remedies can ultimately succeed. The powers conferred by knowledge either become poorly used or used destructively, when the educated mind is in emotional disorder. Religion and politics become a prey to fanaticism when mental health is undermined. Sexual love, domestic life and all human relationships are distorted and robbed of their fundamental security-giving value when exploited at the dictates of psychoneurotic anxieties. Mental health is the major premise of every activity in life, for without a sound mind, judgement is falsified and effort is either inhibited or forced.

We shall, therefore, be taking up what is today increasingly recognized as the most urgent and the ultimate problem facing us, if we pursue the enquiry into the question: 'Where has our psychiatric and psychological science got to in providing an answer to the problems of the sick mind?'

Meanwhile, I will suggest, not a definition, but a characterization of 'mental health' based on the kind of beneficial changes I have observed coming about in patients as a result of adequate

psychotherapy. I will gather these together under three headings.
(1) *Self-confidence,* i.e. freedom to use our powers without internal
hindrance from anxieties which have their origins in childhood.
(2) Increased *capacity to commit oneself* wholeheartedly to full
human relationships and constructive work, i.e. a diminishing of
those fears of being tied, dominated, stifled or overridden in
involvements with other people which make so many folk strive
to achieve a false independence, isolating themselves in a half-in
and half-out way of living, neither doing without nor properly
doing with close relationships with their fellows. (3) Increasing
capacity to stand up to anxiety, and to get over anxiety-producing
events, and not be panicked and driven into an undermining
mental withdrawal from healthy contacts with one's environment.
This conception of 'mental health' implies that enormous numbers
of people are only living half a life, well below their real capacity
for creation, satisfaction and enjoyment. In the end *mental health
is the capacity to live life to the full in ways that enable us to
realize our own natural potentialities, and that unite us with
rather than divide us from all the other human beings who make
up our world.*

CHAPTER TWO

THE TRADITIONAL MORAL DIAGNOSIS

IN 1960 a book was published by an American sociologist, P. Rieff, with the title *Freud: The Mind of a Moralist*.* This title may well surprise many people whose ideas about Freud have only been picked up piecemeal and from popular sources. Freud is generally regarded as having been a daring revolutionary thinker who, in his researches into the nature and working of the human personality in illness, cut across all the polite conventions and social taboos about open enquiry into sexual matters, and told the truth with cold scientific ruthlessness. This truth concerned the antisocial drives and conflicts in our make-up which he regarded as arising from our inherited instincts. I remember many years ago seeing a cartoon in a newspaper in which Freud was shown introducing a pale slim young lady to an enormous anthropoid ape. The caption read 'Freud introduces a young lady to her own unconscious', and the general impression prevailed that Freud was in some way 'against repression of instincts', whatever that might mean. One of the most bizarre distortions of psychoanalytical teaching was the notion that repression being bad, children must be allowed to do exactly as they liked. There was a phase in which some sophisticated pseudo-moderns sought in Freud authoritative backing for a Bohemian revolt from 'respectable' and 'conventional' ways of living.

Needless to say, the life work of one of the world's greatest scientific pioneers cannot be reduced to anything so banal as that. The great biography of Freud by Ernest Jones shows him to have been, in his private life, a man who had no part in such outlooks on social progress. Much of this 'image' of Freud is due to the social atmosphere of the age in which his work broke upon the world. Certainly one of the results of his enquiries has been to concentrate public attention in scientific, literary, and other circles, on sex, and this, aided by the loosening of moral conventions under the impact of two world wars, has led to what many regard as a deterioration of morality. It is possible to find many people today who are afraid to appear 'old-fashioned' if they disapprove frankly of the wholesale flouting of all the normal

* London, Gollancz.

restraints and decencies of behaviour in the name of some supposed sacred right of the individual to be 'himself' irrespective
of the results for other people. One may be accused of being a
'square', though by the time this is in print that term will be
out of date. There is a vague notion that Freud had something
to do with bringing about this state of affairs, though in his
published work he taught unequivocally that 'civilization' must
be painfully built up on the basis of 'renunciation of instincts'.
The fact that in *The Future of an Illusion,* Freud took much the
same ground as Nietzsche, that the strong became criminal by
refusing to tame their instincts, and the weak become neurotic
by being afraid to express them boldly, led to a popular caricature
of psychoanalysis which equated it simply with the idea that
repression of our natural instincts is bad. Thus *Freud: The Mind
of a Moralist* may strike a surprising note for many readers.

Nevertheless, the phrase is strictly accurate. It should be said
that those aspects of a man's work which public imagination
seizes on are not necessarily the most important, nor even the
most revolutionary. Freud took over as his starting-point the
traditional theory of 'human nature as a dualistic whole, involving
an innate and inevitable warfare between 'good' and 'evil'. It is
true that in applying this theory Freud did not use those terms,
though he did say that in the unconscious man is both more
moral and more immoral than he usually appears to be in
everyday living. Nor did Freud place the emphasis, in this dualistic view of man, exactly where earlier thinkers, and 'moral'
public opinion, placed it. Philosophers in the main (for Epicurus
was an exception in one direction, and Nietzsche, and Machiavelli
if he be accounted a political philosopher, were exceptions in
another), and theologians, Christian and Jewish, agreed that our
animal instincts, the 'lusts and passions of the flesh', must be
uncompromisingly disciplined and suppressed. They did not realize what Freud, with his primary concern with mental illness was
forced to see, that the mere suppression of our vital impulse-life
can only result in failure of energy and some form of personality
breakdown. In contrast to the 'official morality' of the Greco-
Hebraic-Christian tradition in our European culture, Nietzsche
took the opposite line that the man who was strong enough to live
out his instincts to the full was the superman who had the right
to dominate the weak who surrendered to the 'slave-morality' of
the Christian. Our modern world has seen this point of view
carried out into ruthless action in political totalitarianism, and
quite openly and consciously cultivated in the practice, and theor-
etically formulated in the theory of legal justice, of the Nazis. The

world has passed its judgement on this 'mental aberration' so far as all free peoples are concerned.

Freud, being primarily a scientist seeking a knowledge of facts, and not a political propagandist, saw that uncontrolled 'instincts' meant criminality, even if over-repressed ones meant neurosis. He taught that civilization was built up on the renunciation of much of our 'instinctive' sexuality and aggression, and reached the view that mental health was to be found along a middle course between the two extremes of licence and repression. He called this middle course 'sublimation'. In other words, the individual became mentally healthy and mature in proportion as he was able to detach sufficient energies of his biological instincts of sex and aggression from their original gross and even destructive aims. The energies of these 'aim-inhibited' instincts could then be redirected to more 'sublime' or socially approved and culturally valuable ends: i.e. they could be 'sublimated'.

In fact, successful sublimation seemed to be extremely difficult to achieve. Freud, therefore, came to the conclusion that psychotherapy involved 'helping the ego', the ordinary self of everyday living at the level of consciousness, against the dangerous strength of antisocial impulses surging up from the unconscious, the home of the instincts, and called by Freud the 'id' or 'it', the impersonal biological substratum of our personality. As we shall presently see, this type of explanation on the basis of 'instinct theory' has become outdated, and a different kind of analysis of human nature is made, which in fact Freud also pioneered. But, assuming the theory of instincts, the work of control and sublimation of impulses seemed clearly to be beyond the power of the unaided individual 'ego', so that a special psychic function, which Freud called the 'super-ego', was developed in childhood to lend powerful aid. Roughly speaking, the super-ego was a technical term for conscience, and it stood for that part of the growing make-up of the child in which there was enshrined within himself the demands and prohibitions of the authorities who had charge of him; the parents who brought him up from infancy, the teachers who educated him according to the standards of his society ('the customs of the tribe'), and finally that vague but omnipresent power called public opinion. We may say that 'conscience' stands for the more mature and realistic part of that disciplinarian function which operates consciously and is considered 'normal', while the Freudian 'super-ego' represents an unconscious, out-of-date, childish function which operates pathologically and produces illness, especially what is known as 'depression'. Freud held that this super-ego is usually too harsh, guilt-inducing and punitively unreasonable, and reflects the anxieties, inexperience and exaggerations to which the child mind is liable. In that case it so sets the individual against himself that he sinks into the paralysed state of depression because all his natural energies have become forbidden to him. Thus, in this diagnosis, the most important aspect of mental illness is the arousal of an irrational, unrealistic, basically childish form of guilt-feeling, which psychoanalysis for very good reasons treats as pathological or disease-producing.

There can be no doubt that in all this Freud was dealing with facts. One does actually find people who suffer from this obsessive self-attack. Most nervous people all too readily take the blame for everything on to themselves, and feel guilty, and feel that everyone else is blaming them, for all that goes wrong. Whether it be the cause or the effect of the unhappy feeling of inadequacy that over-anxious people have, it is certainly there to see and to be explained. It was only Freud's thoroughgoing analysis of the moral and pseudo-moral (or pathologically moral) level of human experience which opened the way to still deeper problems. The 'moral diagnosis' of man's troubles with himself was the age-old one, and it had to be scientifically investigated before anything else could be done. The revolutionary aspect of Freud's work consisted not in his courage to insist on an open-eyed and thoroughly factual investigation of man's sexual life, a matter which should be taken for granted scientifically. Nor did it consist in his theory of the control and management of impulses, and his discovery of the ways in which too drastic 'repression' of our impulse-life led to illness and mental paralysis. His revolutionary work consisted in his determination to make a careful investigation of the actual processes, any and every kind of process that came to light, of man's mental life, instead of indulging in the fervent and dogmatic enunciation of opinions concerning man's social behaviour. Freud's revolutionary work consisted also in his personal and unique skill in discovering the psychological facts, and developing a method of investigation in which the physician and the patient could co-operate in a fully personal way to arrive at an understanding together how and why the patient was so disturbed. Freud developed a method of 'analysing', i.e. 'intellectually' taking to pieces and understanding what was actually going on in our troubled human nature, in the setting of a human relationship in which 'feeling' was free to find open expression, and all with a view to substituting a rational or understandable treatment for mere preaching and condemnation.

Freud was, of course, a child of his own age, and his most important work in psychology dated from 1880 to 1930. He took over at the start the traditional philosophical, theological and popular psychology, especially in the form in which it already appeared to be scientifically sanctioned by the psycho-biological theory of instincts. There was no other point of view from which he could make a beginning. As a result, it is undoubtedly true that he put the 'moral psychology' of the European tradition into a scientific form, which we shall examine more closely in the next chapter. This achievement has, in fact, enabled his successors to go beyond this level of human experience, he himself having provided the initial impetus and suggestions for doing so. The moral level of conflicts over antisocial impulses had to be analysed first in a factual, not in a dogmatic way, if a start was to be made in finding out what really did go on in our troubled mental life. Freud traced our conflicts over so-called 'bad impulses' back to extremely early periods in childhood or infancy. He discovered that they went on in our unconscious dream and phantasy life in terms that were bound up with our childhood experiences of bodily functioning, breast-feeding, excretory processes, genital excitations, and that not only aggressions but also sexual experiences were active in infancy. Associated with all this, he discovered the way in which pathological guilt aroused by a fixed, undeveloping infantile conscience, led to such extreme repression or damming up of psychic energies that vitality could fail and illness supervene. The cure that seemed to be called for would therefore consist of a breaking up of this repression in the unconscious and a re-education of the total self to manage its instincts in more normal ways. Some more detailed aspects of this work we shall examine in the next chapter. In this chapter we are concerned primarily with the 'moral diagnosis' in so far as it is based on the traditional, centuries old view of human nature as containing, innately, bad or antisocial forces which can only be 'civilized' with very great effort and discipline. In this view, which goes back beyond ancient Greece and Palestine, and is found among the early Persian Zoroastrians and in early Oriental philosophies and religions, the innateness of 'bad impulses' is taken for granted. In this respect, Freud, like all his predecessors, did not ask the question: 'Why do men have antisocial impulses, when their basic nature is social?' That Freud's work is still regarded in general as supporting the traditional moral diagnosis, is evident from some recent publications.

Thus a book just published, by Professor O. Hobart Mowrer, Research Professor of Psychology, University of Illinois, is described in the following manner by the publisher: *

* van Nostrand.

'The author has made a searching study of the reasons for the failure of both religion and professional psychiatry in their attempts to deal with the problems of mental and emotional disturbances. He insists that guilt, which is the core of psychological distress, is real and must be accepted as such in order for any therapy to produce beneficial results.'

We shall see that, though guilt is certainly real, it is not true to say that it is 'the core of psychological distress'. Present-day psychodynamic research is telling us another story. The central place given to guilt by Professor Mowrer, and by Freud, is a perpetuation of the centuries old philosophical and theological view of human nature. There must, of course, be very powerful reasons why human thinking did not penetrate deeper than the moral level over so many centuries. This is all the more striking because all the facts necessary for doing so were there to see and were known, but they were not linked up and their significance was not appreciated.

In a word, 'the core of psychological distress' is not *guilt* but *fear*. Guilt is itself a form of fear, but it arises at the stage when the child is becoming socialized and capable of realizing the effect of his actions on other people, and the nature of their reactions of anger and condemnation towards him. He feels ashamed, sad and frightened to find that he has hurt those he loves and needs. There are much more primitive fears than that, fears not of the effects of our *strong* and dangerous needs and impulses, but of our infantile *weakness*, littleness and helplessness in face of an environment which either fails to give the support we needed as infants or else was positively threatening. Human beings all prefer to be bad and strong rather than weak. The diagnosis of guilt allows us to feel that the source of our troubles with ourselves and others is our possession of mighty and powerful instinctive forces in our make-up, which take a great deal of controlling and civilizing. The philosophies of Nietzsche and Machiavelli, and the 'power politics' of the present age, all make it plain that human beings feel at least a secret and often an openly admitted admiration for the ruthless strong man, however 'bad' his ideas and actions may be. In our competitive Western culture (including communism which is every bit as competitive as capitalism) contempt is felt for weakness. We have always known that sympathetic care for the weak and suffering, fostered by Christianity, had to fight its way forwards, and survive on the basis of much compromise; as in the often cited cases of Victorian capitalists who made fortunes by the most ruthless

business methods on the one hand and endowed churches, chari-
ties and hospitals on the other. The main stream of the world's
active life has been carried on in the tradition of the struggle for
power, in which the weakest go to the wall. The superman is
the criminal who has the courage to fight and does not mind
hurting other people. The Christian with his 'slave-morality' of
self-sacrifice to save others is weak and gets crucified. A diagnosis
which traces psychological troubles to our innate strength supports
our self-respect and is what is today called an 'ego-booster'. A
diagnosis which traces our troubles to deep-seated fears and
feelings of weakness in face of life has always been unacceptable.

Democratic ideals have sought to foster the development of a
social outlook in which the poor, the ignorant, the downtrodden,
were to be progressively raised to a higher social level, while the
power of the wealthy was disciplined into social responsibility. So
much was this 'direction of progress' taken for granted in the
early years of this century, that almost inevitable and automatic
'progress' (political, economic and social), towards individual
liberty and equality for all, was taken for granted. It came as a
shock to many well-intentioned people, who had come to feel
that war was a thing of the past, and the world was becoming a
safe and enlightened place for everyone, to discover how thin
this veneer of civilization proved to be when it was shattered by
the first world war. Ever since then, the claims of the strong to
follow out their own will irrespective of their fellows or other
weaker countries, has paraded the world naked and unashamed.
Ours is, and in fact always has been, a world in which it is far
easier to believe that our problem is how to curb and civilize
our strength, than to admit that our troubles arise from our
vulnerability and deep hidden sense of weakness as invididuals.
So the 'moral diagnosis' has always been the favoured one.

This 'moral diagnosis' was made central to the European tradition of thought by Plato and St. Paul. In a chapter contributed
to *Modern Concepts of Psycho-Analysis*,* and entitled 'Man—and
Human Nature,' F. Ashley Montagu (former Head, Dept. of
Anthropology, Rutgers University) writes of the 'traditional man-
view' in our Western culture thus:

'A brief statement of the essence of this tradition would be
that in the western world it is generally believed that man is
both good and evil, but the good is so shot through with the
evil that one must constantly be policing the evil in order to

* Edited by Salzman and Masserman, Philosophical Library, New
York.

give the good an opportunity to express itself. Child-rearing practices, education, religion—indeed most if not all of man's major social institutions testify to the pervasiveness of this view of human nature. Hence the necessity of designing social controls to keep the brute in check so that the amount of trouble into which he gets is kept within more or less manageable bounds.

In the Old Testament man's innate iniquity is already established. 'Behold, I was shapen in iniquity; and in sin did my mother conceive me' (Psalm 51.5) (pp. 45-6).

This view was paralleled by the teaching of Plato, the great Greek philosopher of the fifth and fourth centuries B.C. He illustrated his view of human nature by describing it as like a chariot with two horses and a charioteer. One horse was a many-headed beast of the lusts and passions of the flesh, the other horse was a spirited animal of courage and fighting capacity. The charioteer was 'Reason', the divine principle in man, which made an ally of the fighting animal to help it to rein in and control the many-headed beast. In this twentieth century Freud was to dress that analysis of man in scientific terminology. The many-headed beast became the 'id' or 'it', our impersonal biological nature, the home of the primitive instincts of sex and aggression. The charioteer of reason was no longer a mystic divine principle, a soul which had descended from the world of pure spiritual ideas into the body; it was scientific reason, our conscious thinking self, seeking to rein in our instincts. To help in this struggle, aggression, the fighting animal, was so to speak drawn over on to the side of civilization, and became resident in the 'super-ego', a repressive conscience which captured the individual's aggression and turned it against himself in the interests of law and order.

A similar analysis is implied in the traditional Christian idea of 'body, soul and spirit', and a simplified version is found in St. Paul's contrast of the 'law of the members' and the 'law of the mind'. The law of the members or of the 'carnal mind . . . is not subject to the law of God neither indeed can be' (Romans ch. 8 v. 7). The only possible state, therefore, in which man can exist is one of stern control of our fleshly or animal nature. Man can never be truly in a state of inward peace or genuine maturity, but only in a state of armed truce and cold war, in which conscience must always be strong enough to keep the upper hand. How deeply embedded in our tradition this view is may be seen by reference to the teaching of Hobbes in the seventeenth century that in a state of nature human life would be 'nasty, brutish and short', and by the fact that the teaching of Darwin, defining evolution as a process of the struggle for existence or 'the survival of the fittest', implied that 'fittest' did not mean 'finest in nature and capacity' but only 'fittest to survive', i.e. stronger than all possible enemies.

It may well be that Freud's patient scientific investigation of human living on the basis of this theory, led to the first crack in a theory which functioned as a defensive denial of the deeper realities of human nature. In accepting the necessity for 'renunciation of instincts' in the cause of civilization, and drastic control of instincts by the ego aided by a powerful super-ego, he made the all-important discovery that a far-reaching qualification had got to be made to this philosophy of self-discipline. The self-disciplining function he found could get out of bounds. It could function with such ruthlessness against the rest of the 'self' that it crushed down all vitality and led, not to virtue, but to very serious illness. Freud's psychoanalytic therapy was largely fashioned with the aim of modifying the harshness of the super-ego, and reducing the internal civil war, so that 'rational' controls might be substituted for pathological or disease-producing repressions. In fact, Freud's analysis of human personality on the basis of this 'moral psychology', was, in its theory of the super-ego, the starting-point of investigations which have taken us far deeper into the structure and functioning of the human mind than has ever before been glimpsed.

It must not be thought that all this has made Freud's own initial work unreal. The level of moral conflicts and of pathological disease-producing guilt is really there. Patients usually begin today by presenting the therapist with this kind of problem. In very many cases, the first part and maybe the whole of a patient's treatment by psychoanalysis is taken up with his conflicts in personal relationships, his angers and jealousies and unsatisfied love-needs, which can all be seen to run back into his struggle to maintain himself and get along in a difficult family environment in childhood. It may happen that dealing with these more visible and accessible problems relieves him sufficiently for him to feel able to carry on without further analysis. This makes it necessary that we should devote the next chapter to the orthodox or 'classic' psychoanalysis of Freud, for it is the still necessary and indispensable introduction, not only to most cases of treatment of nervous illness, but also to whatever deeper factors have come to light since Freud's own lifetime.

CHAPTER THREE

THE CLASSIC FREUDIAN 'OEDIPAL' OR 'FAMILY' COMPLEX

WHEN patients come to a psychotherapist or psychoanalyst for treatment, what they complain of at first is roughly either physical symptoms for which their doctor can find no adequate organic cause, or a general state of anxiety, or difficulties in carrying on human relationships because of nervousness and inferiority feelings, bad tempers or sexual problems. In *You and Your Nerves* I sought to give a simple non-technical account of how, step by step, beginning with the physical symptoms, we could uncover the fears behind the symptoms, the resentments and angers behind the fears, the frustrations behind the angers, till at last we found ourselves fairly and squarely faced with the whole complex pattern of the patient's personal emotional life in the setting of the group of human beings who were most important to him. Through symptoms to anxieties, and through anxieties to difficulties in personal relationships: that is the pathway of investigation opened up by Sigmund Freud, in his development of psychoanalysis.

There are, in fact, three kinds of anxiety from which people suffer. The simplest is objectively orientated anxiety over a hostile and unhelpful environment. Then there are two kinds of subjectively orientated anxiety, anxiety over the management of unruly impulses (of sexual desire, aggressiveness, jealousy, etc.) in our reactions to other people, and anxiety over feelings of personal inadequacy, inferiority, weakness and lack of self-confidence in our dealings with other people. By and large, classic Freudian psychoanalysis treated all feelings of anxiety as secondary to and symptomatic of difficulties over the control of instinctive impulses. Feelings of inferiority were explained as due to unconscious guilt over 'bad impulses', and feelings of inadequacy and helplessness to inhibited energies brought about by the drastic repression of such impulses.

There is a level of mental experience on which such explanations hold good. It has become apparent, however, as research has progressed, that we must look deeper for the ultimate explanation of all signs of inadequacy and weakness in the personality. This is held now to have its roots in extremely early obstruction by an unfavourable environment of normally secure infantile ego-development. All feelings of radical weakness must have roots in the helplessness of the baby in a world that fails to support him. This problem we shall turn to in Part 2, but meanwhile we are usually presented by the patient first with the more accessible 'higher level' problems of self-management in his dealings with the people he lives and works with. It was Freud's searching analytical investigation into these problems that opened up the entire modern study of the 'psychodynamic' or emotional and motivational life of human beings.

So far as my experience goes, it seems that the first stage of any thorough psychoanalytical treatment still has to deal with problems of this kind. It is impossible to go straight to the most deeply repressed factors in anyone's personality, and it is a good thing that it is so. As we grow year by year from childhood to adult life, we build up, in our struggles to cope with ourselves and our world, what Freud called 'ego-defences', of which the simplest and best known is the repression of unresolved conflicts deep into an unconscious area of our mental life. We seek to retain in the conscious self of our everyday living only what is reasonably adjusted to our social environment. If we are not able to retain our defence of repression, so that turbulent and disturbed emotions break through into consciousness, and play havoc with our social behaviour, then in our struggle to keep going we are driven into long series of more and more complicated defences piled on defences. Out of all this we develop character distortions, or neuroses, or antisocial, delinquent or even criminal behaviour, or mixtures of all three. If our capacity for feeling for other people, and therefore feeling guilty about hurting them, is reasonably operative, we are more likely to develop neuroses. If our capacity for feeling guilt is severely repressed we are likely to suffer from depression, if it has failed to develop or we cannot tolerate a state of depression, we shall be more likely to act out our hates and frustrated needs in antisocial or maybe criminal ways, or even develop a psychopathic personality.

All this was the stock in trade of the classic pioneering work of Freud, and we must give some account of the explanations he evolved of these problems. The name of Freud will always be particularly associated with the concept of the Oedipus Complex, and in truth this concept was a bold and brilliant way of gathering up into an inclusive theory the substance of what he had discovered. Before Freud, the two main attitudes to children were the sentimental and the dogmatic. They were assumed to be either beautiful little innocents or else cases of 'nature cradled in original sin', and needing the strictest parental discipline. Parents were assumed to be right and to know how to bring up children, and adults could oscillate between the sentimental and the dogmatic view of children as it suited them. Freud, as a scientist simply looking for facts, laid bare all the actual details of the emotional relationships of parents and children. He discovered how intensely 'human' and quite 'unideal' these are.

Children basically *need* their parents, *fear* them if they are angry or too overpowering, *love* them if they meet the child's needs, *resent* them if they are too interfering, and *hate* them if they are hostile or neglectful, and then *feel guilty* towards them, usually with the parents' help in producing this reaction. These needs, loves, fears, hates and guilts, war together in tension-creating conflicts which are beyond the child's capacity to understand or solve. The child in an unsympathetic parental environment can drift ever deeper into internal distress and distortion of personality to become either frankly a 'problem child', or a 'good', quiet inhibited child ill-equipped to face life and liable to neurotic breakdown sooner or later, or an ill child whose repressed tensions are already interfering with bodily health.

It is true that Freud on the whole looked more at the child's attitudes to the parents, than at those of the parents to the children. He seems to have taken over the general opinion of his time that parents naturally and automatically love their children. Thus, in his explanation of the psychological conflicts suffered by children and proving to be the origins of adult neuroses, he laid all the causal blame on the child's *instincts*. Even if that were true, it must be said that the same instincts must in that case operate in the parents also with no guarantee that they have become adequately disciplined, socialized and 'sublimated'. Freud's successors, however, found it inescapable to investigate the attitudes of parents to their children. Parents do not always love their children, sometimes do not even want children at all, or do not want the 'one or two children too many'. Often they treat them as nuisances to be subdued, or lumps of clay to be moulded into whatever shape the parents prefer; and parents can hate their children as well as love them. In fact, parents are not seldom under too great emotional stress themselves to be able to cope calmly and stably with children.

Certainly when parents do not provide the emotional understanding and security needed by their children for non-anxious and self-confident development, it is because the parents are themselves suffering from their own deep-seated anxieties and insecurities. The result of Freud's work has been to show clearly just how intricately parents and children are bound up with each other in networks of complex emotional problems which they cannot understand, and through which they can only stumble blindly along together.

Freud's *instinct theory* led him to formulate the striking and imaginative concept of the *Oedipus Complex* as *the* cause of neurosis. He regarded sexual and aggressive impulses as arising from fixed, inborn, biological drives, and both were bound to operate in full force from birth onwards, all through the particularly formative years of infancy. So much did this concept fasten on the imagination of psychoanalysts that one analyst, Joachim Flescher, suggested the existence of a hypothetical biochemical substance, 'a specific metabolic toxin which I propose to call provisionally "aggression" ',* as the basis of innate destructive drives, so that the 'instinct of aggression' could be viewed as rooted just as firmly in our biological make-up as is sex, and in the same way. The suggestion has never been adopted, and even Freud's own theory of a Death Instinct to account for destructive impulses, failed to convince more than a very small number of his followers (notably Mrs. Melanie Klein). Nevertheless, the view that positive, powerful, inborn instincts of sex and aggression, which generate active impulses purely because this is their nature and not with any reference to the individual's relations with his environment, established itself as the basis of classical psychoanalytical theory and practice.

It was enshrined in the theory of the Oedipus Complex. In Greek mythology, Oedipus, the rejected and castaway son of a Greek king and queen, grows to manhood, returns unwittingly to his native land, kills his father and marries his mother. When he discovers the facts, he is so overwhelmed by guilt, that he puts out his eyes (a symbolic castration) in self-punishment. So, said Freud, every boy baby is fated to want to possess his mother sexually, hates his father as a rival, and becomes overwhelmed by guilt which drives him to give up his sexual love and hate of parents (the 'resolution of the Oedipus Complex'), leave home and marry. Nevertheless, the rejected Oedipus Complex is still active under repression in the unconscious, and neurosis reveals the way in which the problems it creates undermine the erstwhile child in his adult life.

A similar complex (sometimes called the Electra Complex) was held to form in girls, i.e. the Oedipus Complex in reverse, loving father and hating mother. All this is not, naturally, pure inventive imagination. Freud was an accurate observer of what

* *Mental Health and the Prevention of Neurosis*, p. 181.

he found there to be observed. These Oedipal phenomena do occur, and every analyst has come across quite undisguised Oedipal dreams. Guilt and depression are closely linked with these emotional conflicts in the child over his relations with his parents. But theory and research do not stand still, and the Oedipus Complex does not now hold the central place in psychoanalytical theory and practice that it originally held. An American school of analysts (Karen Horney, Erich Fromm, Clara Thompson and others, with the psychiatrist H. S. Sullivan and his followers) have shown that actual Oedipal conflicts in the child are usually forced on him, not by his instincts, but by neurotically possessive parents or parents with whom the child becomes so insecure that he can only cling to them. In the same way, the parallel though somewhat earlier problems associated with the other biological functions of eating and excreting are forced on the child by the emotionally disturbed mother who cannot breast-feed with warm affection and later fusses over the child's food, and the obsessional mother who makes cleanliness training a medium of establishing a control over the child against which he rebels. Similarly, homosexuality is often a variant of the Oedipus Complex where the boy feared and hated his mother and could only turn for love to an affectionate father. W. R. D. Fairbairn has interpreted the Oedipus Complex as a late developed product of the child's inability to grow out of his infantile dependence on his parents. He regards persisting *infantile dependence* as the real cause of neurosis, and the Oedipus Complex as but one of its many, and in this case later, forms, the form in which infantile dependence is very likely to be consolidated round about the fourth and fifth years, to persist into adult life repressed and unconscious.

It must be noted that brothers and sisters also get taken up into this Oedipus Complex as objects of love, hate and jealous rivalry. The Oedipus Complex seems, therefore, to be best if more prosaically named the *Family Complex*. Its many and varied forms and components can then be simply accepted as aspects of the struggle to adapt to family group life, on the part of a child who has not been able early enough to outgrow his infantile dependence on his mother. The view has arisen that the most momentous and critical phase in the baby's development is that in which he begins to grow beyond the two-person relationship of mother-child, into the three-person relationship of mother-father-child, and the multi-person relationships of the parents-children group opening out into the wider community. Fairbairn regards the path of emotional development in human beings as leading from the immature, absolute and one-sided dependence of the new-born babe on the mother to the mature, conditional, co-operative and mutual dependence of adults on one another. It is astonishing how often the examination of difficult personal relationships in adult life, maritally, vocationally and socially, disclose the secret unconscious operation of difficult and disturbed relationship patterns from the family life of childhood.

There can be no doubt that Freud's Oedipus Complex was a brilliant piece of conceptual thinking, and was the appropriate concept for gathering up and formulating the facts that were coming to light at that stage. It is unfortunate that so often in the history of thought great ideas, which in themselves lead on to further exploration, seem to settle into the mass mind to be turned into unchanging dogma and block the way to progress. For many who are not engaged in actual psychodynamic research, but who use the work of Freud to cast light on their own work, in literature, education or what not, Freud has come to be identified with the Oedipus Complex and little else, as if psychoanalysis had stopped dead at that point. Actually, just because it was so true to fact, Freud's great early clinical concept has led on to deeper investigation, by directing attention to what came to be called the 'pregenital levels'. From the Oedipal problems of the third to fifth years, psychoanalysis has probed backwards into the even more complicated problems of the first and second years.

Here again Freud led the way, though he approached these problems of the earliest years also in terms of instinct. Oral instincts were held to drive the infant to seek pleasure and satisfaction in sucking in the first year: and anal instincts drove the infant to seek the pleasure and satisfaction of the exercise of a sense of power in withholding or ejecting faeces, and in waging a battle of wills with mother over cleanliness training. The American 'Culture Pattern' writers already quoted (Horney et al.) and many writers on child psychology, have shown how, in fact, difficulties over feeding and cleanliness are related primarily to the way in which the mother handles and manages her baby. What has increasingly emerged out of the Child Guidance Movement is the overwhelming importance of the mother-child relationship. The latest developments tend to emphasize the fact that this is important, not so much for the satisfaction of the infant's instinctive needs one by one, as for the laying of the foundations of an adequate ego-growth or stable feeling of self-identity. That problem takes us far deeper than the conflicts in the sphere of personal relationships which are typical of the Oedipal level. Yet we have to begin with these simply because, for the most part, they make up the material the patient begins with, when he seeks a psychotherapist's help.

Patient and systematic psychoanalysis, where a good understanding and a trustful relationship grows between the analyst and the patient, can and does lead to great improvements at this level. Physical symptoms, even including stubborn psychosomatic ones (such as duodenal ulcers or sinusitis) can fade away as the patient grows increasingly aware of the fact that they mask, and serve as a means of avoiding recognition of, serious emotional tensions in personal, and basically family, relationships. As these fears, jealousies, rivalries, resentments, hates and frustrations, are steadily talked out and worked over and over, the patient grows in understanding, not only of himself but of those against whom he feels such grievances. His feelings of guilt can subside as he learns to feel more tolerant, first of himself and then of others. He becomes much more able to accept himself in the same straightforward, friendly, understanding way that his therapist does, and becomes able to manage himself in the context of his social and family life with much less strain and anxiety.

Some patients make more progress than others, and nothing in this field works automatically, but I have seldom found a patient who did not derive some help; and in some cases the improvements were far-reaching. This whole question of treatment and its results will be studied in as much detail as is possible in a book of this size, in Part 3. At this stage I wish simply to record my conviction that, though valuable results can come from the 'Oedipal level' analysis, and in a number of cases, this is all that is necessary, nevertheless radical and final results cannot be reached at this stage. The question of how deep one goes with the analysis is decided by the patient. Those who can stop when they find they have reached some point of stabilization through the analysis of their personal relationship problems, do so, usually needing the reassurance that they can come back at some future date, if fresh anxieties arise. Quite often they do not need to. The results in many cases are 'good enough' to satisfy the patient if not the therapist, but by and large this is the level of problems for which relatively short-term psychoanalysis (of from one to three or four years) is suitable. In the early days of psychoanalysis treatments were in general much shorter than they are today, good results being achieved with treatments of about a year's duration. The reason why psychoanalytic treatment tends to last much longer today is basically simply that with the progress of research more and more is known of what there is to treat. One may even say that the Oedipal or 'Family Complex' approach is suitable for much more superficial, but highly important, kinds of treatment carried on at the 'trained social work' level by psychiatric social workers, probation officers, marriage guidance counsellors and so on.

The better the patient's mothering in infancy, or the later in childhood he came to be subjected to serious emotional disturbance, the more adequate is likely to be a treatment confined mainly to the working over of his personal relationships in the light of his early family life. The fact, however, that so many people's troubles have roots that go right back to earliest infancy, is the main reason why psychoanalysis has been driven ever deeper and deeper in the search for basic understanding. It is not mere scientific curiosity but practical need that really motivates all scientific research. Before we follow up this deeper enquiry, we must look more closely at that arresting form of mental illness which above all, in the classic sense, appears as the outcome of unresolved problems of bad impulses in personal relationships, and the unconscious persistence of intense conflicts of love and hate relating to parents in childhood. This is the illness known as Depression, and it is of such outstanding importance that a separate chapter must be devoted to it.

CHAPTER FOUR

DEPRESSION

ONE of the big changes that has come about in medicine in this century is that 'the ill person' has taken the place of 'disease entities'. It is to be hoped that increasing scientific specialization will not reverse this healthy trend and put the clock back in diagnosis and treatment. At one time it was as if illnesses were regarded as self-contained entities, things-in-themselves, which could be treated without any reference to the person who suffered from them. It has come to be more and more recognized that an illness is a disturbed malfunctioning of a person, a human being whose life has had to be carried on in a certain kind of situation, and with a definite history behind him, helpful or hurtful, and an outlook ahead to prospects, encouraging or anxiety-provoking. Illnesses are functions of a number of variable factors in individuals, such as their resources for living, the legacy of their past history both in themselves and in their circumstances, their responsibilities and habits, their ways of life and their fortunes and misfortunes. An illness is not a 'thing' that appears from somewhere to fasten without reason on a chance individual, but in some way it is an expression of that person's life as a whole.

If this point of view has come to the front in physical medicine, to find expression in the idea that we treat the patient, not an entity called 'the illness', it is even more important in psychological illness. There have long been diagnostic labels for different kinds of mental ill-health: the psychoneuroses such as Anxiety-state, Hysteria, Obsessional Neurosis, Phobias, and the psychoses such as Manic-Depression, Paranoia and Schizophrenia. These labels are often critically examined by experts, none of whom pretends to be satisfied with them. None of them can be regarded as representing a clear-cut disease entity, though it is easy to recognize groups of symptoms which make up patterns that are recognizable as hysteric, obsessional, paranoid and so on.

At one time it was customary to speak of *the* hysteric, *the* obsessional, *the* depressed person and so on, and this way of speaking is still in use in the looser language of general conversational discussion. But in fact no such hard and fast typing and labelling of patients is possible. It is true that some patients do develop predominantly symptoms of some one fairly consistent type, such as hysteric or obsessional. Actually, as soon as one begins to investigate the history and the day to day reactions of the ill person, it becomes apparent that he rings the changes from time to time on several or even all of the possible symptom-patterns which our diagnostic labels have isolated. Patients will oscillate between hysteric and paranoid reactions, or hysteric and obsessional symptoms, or will lose some physical hysteric symptom or obsessional ritualistic activity and straightway develop a de-pressed or a detached schizoid state of mind.

The view has been strongly presented by Mrs. Melanie Klein and Dr. W. R. D. Fairbairn that what are called the psychoneuroses ('nerves') with their physical accompaniments of anxiety, their conflicts over impulses and their characteristic mental attitudes (hysteric, obsessional etc.) are in truth ways in which the patient defends himself against some more fundamentally ill condition. These more ultimate forms of illness appear in particularly severe form in the psychoses. We may put the position thus that all the varying forms of mental illness are either defences against, or varying degrees of expression of, one or other of two basic conditions. Depression and Schizoid withdrawnness. These two are not entities and are not mutually exclusive. They are states and reactions of a person under severe emotional stress, not of a transient kind related simply to current events and capable of passing away as the situation changes, but of a deep-seated kind which is the product of the way in which the personality has developed and been shaped from earliest childhood.

We shall leave the Schizoid problem for Part 2, but must here deal with the classic concept of Depression. In this classic sense, depresson is a guilt-illness: one ought to say a 'pathological guilt-illness', for there is a healthy conscience. It is part of maturity of development as a person that one should have become capable of feeling sensitive towards other people's hurts and feeling sorrow over them. If one is oneself the cause of unnecessary suffering to other people, then it is a mature and mentally healthy reaction to be able to criticize objectively one's be-haviour, to feel grieved, reach a judgement that one has 'done wrong' and seek to 'put it right', to make reparation. If that is accomplished satisfactorily, the matter is ended and one is left stronger and wiser. This need to make reparation and preserve good relationships was shown by Mrs. Melanie Klein to play a large part even in some developments of neurosis, which shows how deeply rooted it is in our natural make-up. In theory it might be said that a fully mature person would not behave antisocially and hurtfully to others, and in practice it is true that the more stable a person is, the less likely he is to give unnecessary offence.

We do not, however, deal in theoretical perfections in human beings. We are not always 'at our best' and are liable, particularly under stress, to lapse from adequate standards of consideration for other people. Yet the reasonably mature person is capable of making an apology if it is necessary, and putting matters right. The kind of guilt which plays a part in such experiences is realistic, it is appropriately related to objective facts, and it does not persist unreasonably after matters have been settled satisfactorily.

The kind of guilt found in depression is quite different. Pathological guilt is a compulsive internal cult of self-persecution which cannot be allowed to die down. The depressed person accuses himself over the most trivial things, blames himself for what no one else blames him for, keeps himself on the rack of pseudo-moral self-criticism, feels wicked and worthless as his state of mind gets worse, and sabotages the efficiency of his personality more and more as he goes along. Thus, seriously depressed people can arrive at a state in which they can do nothing but sit and cry in utter misery, feeling rejected by themselves and everyone else, and worn out with their struggle to bear up under this burden of guilt and self-punishment.

Naturally, there are many milder forms and lesser degrees of depression than this, and many people who do not seem to have 'the gift of happiness', who seem to be incapable of finding real pleasure and enjoyment in anything, and who give the impression of plodding on through life in a conscientious and dutiful though basically sad way, are really suffering from some degree of depression. It takes all the joy and spontaneity out of living, and the depressed person feels he only lives half a life, and is never able to fulfil all his potentialities. In *You and Your Nerves* I have given a fuller detailed description of depression. My purpose here is to note its main characteristics with a view to understanding how Freud analysed it and in what way research has gone beyond it to deeper problems.

This serious mental illness came to be the major problem on which Freud focused all his best energies, and until depression was understood it would have been impossible to make any further progress. He began his enquiries with patients who were predominantly hysteric, and showed symptoms, not only of the substitution of physical for mental disturbance (conversion hysteria), but also of 'dissociation' as in hysteric loss of memory and trance-like states, symptoms in which in some way the patient seems to have lost the unity of his personality quite drastically and to have lost touch with himself or some part of himself. All this involved far more complex and deeply buried problems than was apparent in the 1880s and 1890s. Freud's interest turned from hysteria to obsessional neurosis and depression, probably not only from inclination but because it was not then possible to probe deeper into hysteria until obsessional neurosis and depression were thoroughly understood. Hysteria bears the same relation to the 'schizoid problem' as obsessional neurosis does to 'depression', and until depression was adequately studied it was not possible to lay bare the deeper problem.

Whereas hysteria had directed Freud's attention markedly to sexual problems and the cravings arising out of unsatisfied needs for love, obsessional neurosis directed his attention much more to the part played by anger and aggression in mental illness. Not that sexual issues were absent, but sex was seen to be captured by aggression and turned into sadism. The consequences of socially destructive feeling and behaviour had to be faced and questions of conscience forced themselves to the front. It was then that Freud evolved his theory of a parental super-ego (an authoritarian conscience modelled on parents and constituting an internal version of them, embedded in the child's psychic make-up). This super-ego developed to aid the ego in its struggle to subdue and control dangerous and hurtful impulses.

The obsessional character was visibly super-ego dominated, and though this is really no less true of other types of mental organization, it tends in them to be more secret and hidden. The chief features of the obsessional character appeared to be discipline and duty, tidiness and control, conscientiousness and self-organization, and even in more extreme cases a slave-driving attitude towards the self. The super-ego then appeared as a harsh taskmaster keeping a tight hand on our unruly nature, and evoking guilt over every rebellion. This guilt was soon seen to sum up and express the entire structure of a character formed for self-suppression, in a struggle to find a workable solution of the problem of *ambivalence,* a state of mind in which the patient both loves and hates the same person (basically parents) at the same time, and comes to feel in a state of deadlock. He cannot love for hating and he cannot hate for loving. He can only find escape from this dilemma and relief from its intolerable tension, by turning his hate against himself in an effort to free his love to be expressed for others.

Ambivalence, or what we might call a double-barrelled emo-

*tional life of simultaneous love and hate which start up in conflict
as soon as the person enters into any real emotional involvement,
is the basis of classic depression. The pathological guilt felt over
hating someone who is also loved, turns the hate into self-hate,
until all the patient's energy seems to become absorbed in self-
torture and the personality sinks into a paralysed state so far as
external activity goes.* There is, however, plenty of energy available
for the attack on the self. In extreme cases the only activity that
seems to be left to the patient is a secret intense self-accusation
and self-punishment, in a personality which is more or less
immobilized and out of touch in relation to the external world.
One of the far-reaching insights with which Freud penetrated the
hidden secrets of this seriously disturbed mental condition, was
his observation that the patient (i.e. originally the child), not
being able to tolerate hating his external love-object in reality,
mentally 'internalized' him. That is to say he took the bad side of
his love-object, as it were, into himself, and identified himself
with it. He could then hate the bad parent inside himself, which
was at the same time self-hate or turning of his hate inwards,
and love the good parent in his outer world. This, however,
belongs to the more detailed clinical refinements of psychoanalysis.

It is not surprising to find that depressed people alternate
between depression and bad temper. It is just as intolerable to
hate onself as to hate one's parent on whom one's security
depends. The quickest way to gain relief from this crippling self-
hate is to turn it outwards again, to direct it away from oneself
and back against other people once more. This can for a time ease
the mind, for the hate need not be directed back against the
parent who is its true object, but against anyone or anything else
which can serve as a substitute target. I had one patient who at
the beginning of analysis consciously hated her father and loved
her mother, who was a most domineering woman. In due course
it came home to her that it was really her mother she had hated
most as a child, but dared not show this and so had joined with
the mother in directing all hostilities against father. A more easily
worked arrangement is to export the hate outside the family circle,
as in the case of a patient who was devoted to a difficult mother
but hated a distant aunt of whom she knew little and whom she
rarely saw.

Thus in a superficial sense, if you give a depressed person
some reason to be angry with you, you give him a means of
escaping for a short time from his depression: but not for long,
for he soon begins to feel guilty and hates himself once more. For

this reason, depressed people often make good crusaders. They can be aggressive on behalf of other people's wrongs without feeling guilty, but they cannot fight their own battles without succumbing to pathological guilt and falling ill. Many a fanatical fighter for a good cause is depressed at heart, and cannot afford not to have some cause to fight for. It is this, and not only genuine differences of opinion on policy, that stokes the fires of political controversy and animosity. It is not, of course, true to say that *all* fighters for good causes must be depressed people, but those who are not depressed go about it in a different spirit and with less rancour.

I think it is undoubtedly true that depression of the classic type does not occur as often, at any rate in its more clear-cut forms, as it used to do. I think this is due to a far-reaching change in cultural attitudes to guilty feelings, as compared with, say, Victorian times. This may well be due to the fact that the older evangelical religious beliefs in hellfire, sin, guilt before God, and eternal punishment, have lost the hold they had fifty years ago. In those days, a common symptom of extreme depression was the conviction of having committed 'the unforgivable sin'; it is a long time since I heard a depressed person express that symptomatic conviction. It is likely that most people today, depressed or otherwise, have never heard of this particular New Testament reference. Moreover, the whole climate of public opinion concerning morality has changed as compared with Freud's day and generation. Many of the classical novels of that era were written round themes of moral wrong and sin, and offences of sexuality and aggression. Thus, in George Eliot's 'Adam Bede', the centre of the whole story is the young squire's adultery with Hetty Sorel and her deportation to a convict settlement for the murder of her baby. These themes, so close to the atmosphere of classic depression, are no longer the stock in trade of the novelist. He is more concerned with characters who suffer from feelings of the futility and emptiness of life. In general conversation one is more likely to find people adopting the attitude of 'I couldn't care less' rather than admitting to feeling guilty, a change that is not necessarily an improvement.

The religious cultivation of 'conviction of sin' certainly often did lead to a confusion between religious experience and pathological depression. Martin Luther suffered severely from depression, which he interpreted solely in religious terms, but which today would be diagnosed as an illness.* But, if it be true that some cultural, moral and religious forces played a part in maintaining depression of the classic illness variety, it is more important to

* Cp. *You and Your Nerves*, p. 98.

take note of the fact that today the analysis of psychological illness has penetrated to a deeper level. It is now apparent that depression is not the final and ultimate form of illness it was once held to be, but can actually be maintained as a defence against a state of mind that is even more feared.

I do not think it is true that traditional moral and religious teaching created and maintained pathological depression, but rather that they were themselves involved in a general attitude to human nature in which a much more subtle problem is to be found. I have already made it clear that I regard the age-old moral diagnosis of human troubles as due to an intense need not to have to acknowledge 'weakness', even if that escape is bought at the price of having to admit 'badness'. The truth is that man's universal preference, in an insecure world, for feeling strong even if it involves being bad, rather than good and weak, tied both philosophy and religion, and also general public opinion all down the ages, to 'the moral diagnosis'. Freud also accepted this diagnosis, with the result that depression came to be the centre of his investigations, as indeed it had to be, for otherwise, until it was investigated, it barred the way to further understanding. He analysed it in so thorough a way that he made it inevitable that his successors would be able to probe behind this illness to its most hidden roots.

The International Journal of Psycho-Analysis in 1960 contained a symposium on Depression in which some contributors still held simply to the established, classic view. Others, however, showed that there are increasing signs of awareness that that view does not give us the whole truth about this illness, and that other and very different factors must now be taken into account. It is a significant fact that Freud, after having based his theory all through on a doctrine of instincts and conflicts over the management of impulses, is found in his very last book, a book which he was not able to finish, bringing up the all-important problem of ego-splitting, or the fundamental loss of internal unity of the self. It is in the last and unfinished chapter of the book that he embarked on this theme, pointing out that ego-splitting occurs not only in the psychoses but in the psychoneuroses also. One cannot help but feel sad over the fact that Freud was deprived by great age of the chance of following up in a radical way this development of theory and clinical investigation, for which his own earlier work had prepared the ground: and we have been deprived of his insight working on this problem. Yet he clearly envisaged the development of ego-psychology beyond the point reached by his own writings of the 1920s.

Freud had, for the most part, regarded the ego (the 'I' or personal self) as a relatively superficial thing, a 'psychic apparatus' set up to control the unruly instinctive impulses which surged up out of the impersonal unconscious or 'Id'. The problems of ego-splitting, however, call for a much more fundamental theory of the ego as standing for the primary natural wholeness and unity of the entire person, which then becomes split into mutually hostile parts as a result of bad early experiences, leading to internal psychic conflict. The pristine unity must be there at birth in however primitive and rudimentary a way, as Fairbairn holds. The subsequent history of the child can then be envisaged, not as a struggle to get a number of separate instincts satisfied, but as a process of ego-development, which, ideally, should lead to the growth of a strong and well-established self-identity, a self-confident personality.

The resulting view of mental illness will then be, not that of a problem of frustrated instincts, but of the basic weakness caused by the obstruction and failure of ego-development. The 'person-as-a-whole' is left by an unsatisfactory childhood in a state of feeling quite inadequate to cope with life. In the symposium referred to, Elizabeth Zetzel said that the new factor in modern theories of Depression was the ego. In fact, most of the writers who recognized that, oscillated between explanations of depression in terms of ambivalent love-hate conflicts creating guilt, and explanations which endeavoured to do justice to the fact that depressive illness so often discloses what are called 'regressive' characteristics. The patient is seen to be breaking down into an involuntary or internally enforced retreat from life, a mental 'running backwards' away from the adult external world with which he feels unable to cope. He is in desperately anxious search for a safe refuge, in which a return to infantile dependence in some form could be made the starting point for recovery.

In 1962, in a paper in *The International Journal of Psycho-Analysis*, entitled 'The Manic-Depressive Problem in the Light of the Schizoid Process', I set out reasons for holding that *Depression*, the struggle with hate and guilt, was but the 'top layer' of a more fundamental illness of the nature of *Regression*. The patient, however gifted and capable in his workaday personality or adult ego, is undermined by the legacy of a weakened ego of infancy. His 'whole ego' is split, the problem Freud had begun to explore further at the close of his life. It may be said here that the term 'splitting' is quite appropriately used of the 'ego', even though this is a psychic entity or organization. Thus, when a group of dissident members 'split off' from their parent organization owing to some disagreement over policy, they are referred to as 'schismatics' or as a 'splinter group'. The word 'schism' is the same root-word as is used in 'schizoid', and in psychodynamic theory this problem of 'ego-splitting' is termed 'the schizoid process', which we have referred to several times already. We shall turn in Part 2 to its closer examination.

At this point we may conclude this chapter on Depression by observing that patients frequently oscillate between depressed and schizoid states of mind, and depression turns out to be a defence against the onset of this deeper trouble. We may say that the patient prefers to force himself to 'stay put' and face the accusers who, he feels, are attacking him both inside and outside himself, and therefore to feel 'ill with guilt', than to find himself plunged into a headlong mental 'running away' from life into a self-isolated, detached, and frighteningly unreal state of mind which is harder to face than depression.

CHAPTER FIVE

PSYCHOLOGY AND MORALS TODAY

IN view of what has been said about the classic Freudian psycho-analytic theory, and indeed traditional psychology in general, being a moral psychology, it may be as well to deal briefly with the question of the bearing of modern developments in psycho-dynamic theory on moral problems. We have already noted that in spite of the fact that Freud's basic theory was that human troubles are due to the unruly nature of what are often popularly called our 'animal instincts' (as set forth in his essay 'Civilized Sexual Morality and Modern Nervousness' 1908, and 'The Future of an Illusion' 1927), psychoanalysis and the modern psychological approach in general are often accused of undermining morality and personal responsibility. This may occur in two ways. Firstly it may be said: 'My instincts are what they are, I can't help their being antisocial, and if I repress them I shall fall ill.' Freud's theory of 'sublimation of instincts' is too subtle and complex to have much force with anyone disposed to argue that way, and whatever sublimation may mean, Freud himself plainly held that the great majority of human beings do not 'sublimate' with much success. I believe, in fact, it is true that 'instinct theory' does obstruct the development of a sensible and realistic morality, both as regards sexual and aggressive behaviour; though this is most easily illustrated by reference to sex, the problem is exactly the same in principle as regards aggression. In practice, indiscriminate sexual behaviour is now much more tolerated than indiscriminate aggressive behaviour.

This whole question would be clarified at once if we could agree on what we mean by morality. I can only state simply the position I shall take in this discussion. By morals I mean, not a set of supramundane and absolute ethical principles, the same for all ages and races, and to be unvaryingly imposed without any qualifications on all human beings alike, unless, by being insane they can be deemed to be incapable of moral responsibility: I mean simply the ways in which a reasonably mature human being naturally behaves towards other people, i.e. the ways common-sense shows we must behave if proper respect is to be paid to the rights of 'individual personality' in each and all of us.

We ought to distinguish sharply between *moral values* and *moral condemnation*. Condemnation has a limited practical utility as a protest against someone's hurtful behaviour to others. But we have to face the fact that moral condemnation, carrying with it the punishment of moral sanctions (whether in religious, ethical or legal forms) to enforce obedience, has never yet succeeded in solving the problem of antisocial behaviour. At best it only puts a curb on it. The reasonably mature, non-anxious person does not need sanctions to make him behave well. The very disturbed person who is motivated by deep-seated fears, is driven into anti-social behaviour by causes which are not reached or affected by moral condemnation and punishment. The community has a clear right to protect itself by physically enforced constraint when antisocial behaviour goes beyond a certain limit, but none of this solves the problem of 'immoral activity' *per se*. I would regard it as self-evident that intelligent human beings will develop fairly clear ideas of how their life together is best to be lived, and that these ideas will be formulated as 'moral values'. I take moral values to be positive goals, genuine ideals to guide our educational endeavours, and though they will not necessarily be defined in exactly the same way in different ages and cultures, yet they will have a basic common element at all times.

Moral condemnation, however, uses moral values, not as guides, but as a whip to beat the disturbed, antisocial person with. The psychotherapist never does that. He seeks to understand, to explain, to promote insight in the person who has got into bad relations with his fellows, and in a sympathetic setting which, by making possible the allaying of fears, also makes possible the redevelopment of the personality in a more happily socialized way. When we come to deal with individuals we have to remember that every person has a history, which may well have left him literally not able to rise to the level of consistently mature social behaviour. Such a person needs help and not just blame.

Thus we come to the second way in which it is often held that modern psychology undermines morality, by undermining moral responsibility. If 'instinct theory' gives some an excuse for saying: 'I can't help my instincts being what they are', so it is thought that the psychotherapeutic approach gives others the excuse of saying: 'I can't help what my history and upbringing have been, and if they have made me treat other people badly, you must put up with it and understand me sympathetically.' I do not think that either of these objections have any substance *in practice*. Those who are going to behave antisocially in fact, will do so whether they can or cannot find excuses of this kind. Psycho-

therapy assumes that the person, by coming for treatment, wants
to be helped in this matter, and actually the general experience
is that those who seek psychoanalysis, unless they are markedly
paranoid (and then they do not usually seek treatment), are either
genuinely distressed over their inability to control their emotional
outbursts, or else distressed at their tendency not to feel enough
concern, a state of mind which they feel ought not to be.

Moral questions concerning aggressive behaviour are far easier
to deal with than those which concern sexual activity. There is
usually a considerable degree of tolerant understanding for the
persistently irritable and aggressive person, and I have often been
impressed by the degree of tolerance with which aggressive
outbursts by some of my patients have been received by those
with whom they lived or even worked. Beyond a certain point,
however, aggression is usually met with a sharp counter-attack
which reminds the disturbed person that toleration has its limits.
It is in the region of sexual questions that it appears to me that
'instinct theory' is particularly misleading. If we suppose ourselves to be endowed with what Freud called 'the mighty sexual
instinct', then two schools of thought will arise, in fact have
arisen. Victorian morality developed a puritanical ethic of rigid
and narrow control of such a dangerous psychic force. Since the
first world war public opinion and practice have swung very far
the other way. The social upheavals consequent on two world
wars have broken down old conventions, made indiscriminate
sexual experimentation much easier and more generally tolerated,
and created a climate of opinion which regards it as of no serious
consequence. The very notion of sexual morality has come to be
held by many to be old-fashioned and out of date. If there's a
baby, never mind, get it adopted. Casualness and the 'couldn't
care less' attitude with many infects one of the most important and
intimate of all human relationships. The Victorian horrified taboo
on all premarital physical intimacy arose out of a fear of sexuality,
and the intense sense of guilt with which everything sexual was
loaded often operated as much inside marriage as outside, destroy-
ing all happy spontaneity and natural reaction. Thus one married
couple, deeming sex to be animal, carnal and 'of the flesh' and
unspiritual, had one planned act of intercourse when they decided
it was their duty to have a child, and then waited to see whether
a pregnancy had resulted. This can only be understood as a case
of neurotic anti-sexuality calling for profound sympathy at such a
suppression of all natural vitality.

The pendulum of opinion, however, now seems to have swung
over to the idea that instincts have a kind of divine right not to

be thwarted, a right which, nevertheless, is not as freely conceded to aggression as to sex. If we really had to believe in this 'thing' called 'the mighty sex instinct', I do not think it would be easy to combat this attitude. If it were really true that here is a tremendous biological drive which must be given free expression if illness is to be avoided, it would be hard to see on what grounds sexual activity could be confined rigidly to the narrow limits of monogamous marriage. If human nature were really so unfortunate as to be at the mercy of such a force, I do not think we could do anything very effective about its moral control *en masse*. Policies of enforced control never do prove to be very effective. Widespread concern is being voiced today in medical and social reports about the rising percentage of premarital pregnancies and of illegitimate babies, babies, I would prefer to say, brought carelessly into the world, with no trouble taken to ensure for them their birthright, the provision of a whole and stable background of two parents who really want them. It would surely be better to base practical sexual morality, not on the management of the 'sex instinct', or even on the performance of the sexual act, but on mutual consideration and on the inalienable rights of the baby to a proper parental environment. Contraception does not enter into this question at this point, for obviously many people do not bother to use it. As a matter of 'moral values' the fact that we reject Victorian rigidity with respect to sex, does not imply that we must agree that uncontrolled and irresponsible sexual activity is a good thing. We do not so regard uncontrolled aggression, why then sex? Sensible self-management with due consideration to others is a good thing that we normally expect of both adolescents and adults in other spheres; why not then in sex, especially when it comes to irresponsibly risking the creation of another human being, and the likelihood of his coming unwanted into the world. Even if we consider only the two parties to the immediate relationship, is it desirable that such a tremendous experience as the birth of a young woman's first baby should occur in circumstances in which she may not want to marry the father, or else feels forced to; or would have to choose between parting with her baby or bringing him up without a father? It is out of this situation that many of the highly disturbed personalities of the next generation will come. This appears to me to be the most important consideration so far as teaching sexual self-control as a moral value is concerned.

As soon as we begin to deal purely with the individual's behaviour and the sexual impulse *per se*, we must think in quite different terms. To talk about a 'powerful sex instinct' is to encourage young people to think that sex is bound to be a problem in itself, and that is not the case. There is no clinical reason for believing that innately antisocial instincts of sex and aggression requiring tremendous control, exist in reasonably mature and self-assured persons. Sexual and aggressive activities have an instinctive basis, but they are functions of human beings as whole persons, they are not separate entities arising out of our biological make-up as a threat to the personality. The way our sexuality and aggression operate in practice is determined by the state our personality as a whole is in at the moment: and that in turn, as we shall see, depends on the extent to which fears dominated our lives in the early formative, impressionable years. In the case of aggression, if the grip of fear is too absolute, aggressive reaction may be completely inhibited, and the unhappy individual may be rendered unable to stand up for himself when necessary. On the other hand, in the course of growing up, the struggle to master a legacy of fear from the earliest years can easily lead to the over-stimulation of aggressiveness, and we get the equally unhappy person who is always on the defensive, always attacking, doomed to wreck every friendship by temper outbursts, and in general hostile to all and sundry. Yet again, the person who has grown up secure of affection and with normal self-confidence, is slow to anger, does not easily take offence, is patient with provocations, and if really driven to anger is aggressive in a realistic way which dies out when danger is removed. We are not dealing here with an innate, destructive instinct always straining at the leash, but with an instinctive potentiality for reacting in ways either appropriate to the circumstances or else determined by the disturbed internal conditions of our personality.

It is in this light that we must see sex. It is an instinctive potentiality which is far from being an unvarying powerful drive all the time demanding an outlet. In fact, like aggression, its practical expression varies with the circumstances and the state of mind of the person concerned. In a personality in the grip of deep-seated neurotic fears, sexual response may be inhibited al-together, and the female will suffer from frigidity and the male from impotence. Where deep-seated fears of early origin have been fought down in the struggle to achieve an active personality, sexual response may be over-stimulated and exploited; so that in the habitually aggressive person sexuality becomes sadistic, a drive for domination over another human being in which success acts as an ego-booster. Yet again, if early fears have led to the growth of a very withdrawn, detached, aloof personality, the unhappy individual feels lonely, isolated, and out of touch with his world. He may then be driven to seek to compensate for his inability to get in touch on a mental, personal level by exploiting physical, sexual contacts instead. If, however, we consider the reasonably secure, non-anxious and friendly person, we shall find that sex is not an obsession or a social nuisance, but an instinctive potentiality which takes its normal place among all the other interests and functions of the whole person. Sexual response will not be indiscriminate, but realistic and appropriate as an expression of genuine affection, and capable of sensible control where that is necessary. In the cases where sexuality arises in problem form, little good is likely to be done merely by moral condemnation. There is a serious personality problem to be understood, and it will always be found that if a person's sexuality is disturbed, that will not by a long way be the only aspect of his personality that is functioning unhappily; it will be part of a larger whole. The fact that we must set out to understand the sexually disturbed individual, does not, however, absolve us from recognizing that the sexual behaviour of the stable person enshrines proper moral values, or implies standards of behaviour that we cannot but recognize as proper to sound human living.

PART 2

DEEPER UNDERSTANDING

CHAPTER SIX

PRIMARY FEARS AND THE
WITHDRAWN PERSONALITY

THE analysis given so far of what used to be called 'Nerves' and is now more correctly known as 'Emotional Illness' or Personality disorder, may be called the classic or orthodox diagnosis. As far as it goes it is all true, but we are bound to admit that no kind of treatment hitherto based on this diagnosis has been able to produce complete 'cures'. I am not referring here only to psycho-therapeutic treatments, for all the moral and legal procedures which have been evolved by civilized societies have also been attempts to 'cure' men of their antisocial impulses. While moralists and legalists have sought discipline and control of impulse in the interests of social order, and Freudian psychoanalysis, in its earlier form at any rate, sought 'sublimation' or redirection of the energies of such impulses to positive social uses, no way has been found of 'curing' men of these so-called antisocial impulses themselves. Indeed the classic theory precludes the very idea of such cure for it regards them as inborn.

This is not to say that no good results of such legal, moral and psychotherapeutic treatments have been secured. It would be absurd to say that. Behaviour has been kept within reasonable limits with the majority of people (at any rate in times of peace). By the various psychotherapeutic and psychoanalytic methods the symptoms of conflict in the personality have been relieved to varying extents and some individual persons have been helped to grow more stable and better adjusted to life. Yet it is a story of partial success, and failure to secure the really radical results desired. Always there has been a deep level of disturbance in the personality that somehow was not reached.

Research, however, has not halted at the classic diagnosis. In the 1920s Freud himself began to move on beyond his theory of instincts and turn his attention to the study of the 'personal self' or 'ego' as it is technically called. Even then he was mainly preoccupied with the problem of the struggle over bad impulses, and the problem of guilt and depression they set up. Nevertheless, a new point of view or line of approach had come into being which was destined to lead far deeper into the workings of the human mind. Freud's great life-work consisted in the exhaustive analysis of the problems of antisocial impulse, control and failure of control, guilt and repression and self-punishment, and finally the end result of it all, that paralysed state of mind we know as Depression. We have seen that this old diagnosis of the human predicament taught by Plato and St. Paul, had to be investigated thoroughly before any further advance could be made.

But Freud also went on to open a way for his successors to go deeper, into what are known as the problems of the schizoid, 'cut off', withdrawn and detached personality; or in milder forms, the shy, timid but otherwise unemotional person who somehow seems to be 'shut up' inside himself. Depression, as we have seen, is the result of the conflicts of love and hate. It is the state of self-punishing grief consequent on finding oneself feeling 'bad' impulses, greedy or angry, sexual or aggressive, in apparently uncontrollable ways, towards those whom we also love. Depression arises in general from the problem of antisocial and destructive impulses threatening to break out, or actually breaking out, indiscriminately in everyday life. This problem ranges from irritability and bad temper to delinquency and crime. It is often disguised and rationalized in ruthless economic competition and in political hates and fanaticisms. Depression arises out of the failure to control 'man's inhumanity to man' in those who possess some normal sensitiveness about causing suffering to other people. The 'ability to be depressed', if we may put it that way, shows that some degree of development of the capacity to feel for others has taken place early in childhood, and implies that there is a deeper and more primitive level of emotional life than that.

At various points in *You and Your Nerves* glimpses of a different kind of problem appeared. Behind the intense mental conflicts and *active* suffering of the psychoneuroses or nervous illnesses, in which the patient is visibly struggling in a welter of urgent needs, violent angers, paralysing guilts and anxieties, there lies, largely hidden but periodically breaking through, the *passive* suffering of exhausted and apathetic states of mind. In *You and Your Nerves*, pages 29-30, I described the symptoms of fatigue and lack of energy in which the normally active self seems to be replaced by a passive and lifeless one. On pages 54-6 the symptom of claustrophobia was described with its acute anxiety about being 'shut in'. This was shown to be a reaction against the opposite symptom of agoraphobia, the fear of going out. Here a frightened self has withdrawn from a dangerous and alarming world to seek safety inside a small safe place from which it fears to emerge again. Here also the normally active self seems to have been given up in favour of an inactive one which is overwhelmed with anxiety if it ventures forth to face the outer world. Thus a patient described how she stepped out of her front door one morning to go shopping and was suddenly assailed by a rush of fear and ran inside again. This happened quite unexpectedly and involuntarily.

On pages 66-70 it was shown how the child can become fundamentally overstrained, fear-ridden and weakened in the midst of the menacing pressures of life in an unsympathetic, unloving or even violent family group. Such a child shrinks into his self, 'goes into his shell' as we say, to find protection or escape from emotional injuries. Many people even today do not seem to realize that to allow a tiny child to suffer a prolonged, emotionally disturbed state of mind can inflict a permanent injury on his personality. Recently in a radio play a child was made to say 'It doesn't matter what you do to me now, you can't hurt me any more.' That could only mean that the foundations of an outwardly hard and unfeeling but inwardly supersensitive personality had already been laid. On pages 92-4 a contrast was made between a part of our whole self that still carries the legacy of the emotional injuries of childhood and is, in effect, a badly hurt child partly withdrawn on his own account, and partly repressed and kept there while the struggle goes on to build up another part of our whole self which shall be a second, adult self functioning in consciousness. Many people become very aware of a fear-ridden child within them, never more poignantly expressed than by Coleridge in the poem *Dejection*.

On page 104 reference was made to the schizoid, cold, aloof personality which seems to have lost the capacity both to love and hate, and for whom the experience of personal relationship is distressingly thin. On page 115 we took note of the signs of an underlying inactive part of the personality, causing a failure to develop energetic drives and active powers, inhibiting spontaneity and sapping initiative, while on pages 122-3 it was indicated that *all these phenomena, so different from the guilt-producing conflicts, have their roots in fear: not fear of disapproval as a secondary result of trouble over bad impulses, but fear in a primary sense, the fear of the small and helpless human child at the mercy of a bad environment.*

In the later work of Freud, and in that of Mrs. Melanie Klein, psychoanalysis underwent a change of emphasis from sex to aggression and we have now to make clear that a further change of emphasis is coming about, from both sex and aggression to basic and elementary fear as the root cause of all psychological disorders. The ruling idea with Freud was that human beings were born with inherited needs expressed as definite drives or impulses demanding 'gratification'. This notion of 'demand for gratification of instincts' was the key concept which dominated the first half of Freud's work (1880-1920) especially in the form of specific needs for sexual gratification. The frustration of these sexual needs filled the organism with tension and the mind with angry protest. Freud originally regarded the disturbing factor of angry emotion and aggressive impulse as a result of sexual frustration, but from 1920 onwards he advocated a different and more specialized version of this aspect of our make-up, namely an innate *destructive instinct*, or death instinct as he called it, which he put alongside and on an equality with the sex instinct as the trouble maker.

At the same time, however, in turning his attention more definitely to the 'personal self' (the 'ego'), he had begun to prepare the way for the idea of the 'gratification' of particular instincts to fall into the background. The problem of the wholeness and integrity of the personal self came more and more to the forefront. Psychoanalysis began moving towards a phase in which the loss of unity in the self (the 'splitting' of the personality or ego, as it has come to be called), appeared as a more important cause of psychological disorder than lack of gratification of particular instincts. The work of Mrs. Melanie Klein, who first extensively used 'play' to understand the unconsciousness of the child, furthered this trend in the 1930s. She concluded that sex only causes trouble when it gets mixed up with aggression, i.e. that not sex *per se* but the sexual drives of an angry and aggressive person are what prove difficult to control. The emphasis was shifted decidedly on to Freud's new concept of an instinct of aggression, an innate destructive drive or death instinct as the case of neurosis. With Mrs. Klein, as with Freud, anxiety was held to be largely a secondary reaction, a fear of our antisocial drives breaking out of control. Accordingly, *passive* states of personality were explained as due to the repression and inhibition of the *active* sexual and aggressive energies through guilt.

But it is now clear that the story does not end there. More and more in the last twenty years schizoid and schizophrenic states have forced their way into the centre of clinical and research interest. In clinical practice they are unavoidable. In the 1940s

Dr. W. R. D. Fairbairn of Edinburgh came to the conclusion that
far more people suffered from the problems of the schizoid or
withdrawn personality than from depression, and he worked out
a radical revision of psychoanalytical theory from this point of
view. He described the detached or shut-in person as appearing,
under psychotherapeutic treatment, like a small timid mouse
venturing a little way out of his safe hole into the dangerous
world outside and then rushing back in alarm. He came to the
conclusion that the inner hard core of neurosis was not Freud's
Oedipus Complex in which the child struggled with sexual and
aggressive impulses felt towards his parents, but prolonged and
unconscious or repressed 'Infantile Dependence' with all its implications of fear, weakness and arrested development in face of
an overpowering and dangerous world. Put simply, and in view of
the extremely widespread extent of 'nervous illness' recognized
today as a fact, this means that human beings are not anything
like as successful in growing up as we generally believe ourselves
to be. It seems rather that we do not so much grow out of childhood as grow over the top of it, and preserve it deep within our
unconscious mental life.

The position is reached then that *emotional illness is not basically due to the frustration of the need for gratification of particular
impulses, or the anxiety and guilt of the fight to obtain it. That
is incidental to a larger problem, that of the struggle, set up as a
result of too early fear, to develop a strong whole personality
adequate to coping with the outer world in adult years.*

My own view is that this is a true but also an extremely un-
welcome conclusion. Why is it that thinkers, philosophers, theologians, moralists, educationalists, scientists and ordinary general
opinion, have for centuries held fast to the belief that the cause
of our troubles is to be found in powerful active 'bad' or antisocial instincts which are regarded as part of our inborn make-up?
I have already stated that I believe the real reason is that if we
must admit that there is something wrong in our human nature,
we would all rather find that it is something which, even if it
is bad, is at any rate powerful and strong. We do not want to
discover that the root causes of our problems are to be found
in deep-seated fears and feelings of weakness. We would rather
feel bad but strong than frightened and weak. Thus one patient
who was seriously terrified by exceptionally cruel treatment as a
child, and had become very markedly turned in on herself, was
scared of the other children at school and felt a great need of
support from the teachers. This she tried to get by working hard,
being a good girl and causing no trouble, only to find that she

was taken for granted. This made her feel so insecure that, when she moved to another school, she suddenly became a ring-leader in mischief, was in constant trouble for rebelliousness, and got all the attention she so badly needed. Another patient who, as the slighted member of the family, felt inferior and grew up shy and timid, suddenly produced a bad 'mental breakdown' in her teens in which she shocked everyone by cursing God, her parents and family, and was at once taken serious notice of. She commented to me: 'If I wasn't bad, I wasn't anything at all.'

Thus man has fallen into the greatest and subtlest of all self-deceptions and rationalizations of his plight, the idea that we are born with instincts that, by the verdict of thousands of years of history, are basically antisocial and only very superficially civiliz-able. I do not myself see any convincing clinical evidence that that is true. I see no proof that sex and aggression are an inevitable source of trouble in a normally self-confident and non-anxious person. Just as Melanie Klein found that sex only became trouble-some when fused with aggression, so my observation is that *both sex and aggression only become troublesome when they are stimulated by fear; and arise as part of a defensive struggle to master fear and flight from life, by exploiting any active capacity which can be used in any given situation.* By fear, I do not mean here the realistic fears of adult life which would normally be faced in an adult way. I mean *the legacy of deep-buried fears of infancy and early childhood which can undermine the most capable individual from within.* Once fear has laid its grip on the tiny infant in his most impressionable and mouldable years, once he comes to shrink away mentally from this environment before he is big enough to stand up to it, because it feels to him to be hostile and menacing, no natural and innate capacity can thereafter function and grow normally. I do not believe that human nature is innately antisocial. So far as I can see the study of schizoid problems proves conclusively that Freud was wrong in believing that human nature is inherently destructive and egocentric, that human beings are not prepared to be other than unruly, and that civilization can only be imposed by force. (Cp. S. Freud, *The Future of an Illusion.*) It was perhaps the one great disservice he did to lend his great authority to such ideas. All that is ever imposed by force is reluctant submission, never true civilization. That so much genuine social feeling, love and friendliness can survive at all in the midst of all the dangers and insecurities of human life seems to be strong evidence that human nature is not basically antisocial; rather, that human beings are formed for and will naturally develop good and co-operative relationships if they have the chance; i.e. if they have the good fortune to grow up as children in families where personal relationships are secure and affectionate. But they will grow destructive and egocentric in proportion as fear gets an early and deep hold on them.

I agree with Fairbairn who holds that aggression is not a primary response of the infant and does not arise independently of frustration; and with Ginsberg, the sociologist, who writes:

'I incline to the view that aggression is not a primary tendency to hurt or destroy, but rather an intensified form of self-assertion and self-expression, brought into play under conditions of obstruction, or of loss of independence. . . . If that be so, aggression and ill-will generally may be a secondary result of thwarting and interference.'*

Thus, if children grow up in environments that constitute a menace to the integrity of their own proper selfhood, then they will be perpetually 'on the defensive', hypersensitive to the possible existence of threats, seeing dangers where none exist, creating difficulties by expecting them, and unwittingly manufacturing their own evidence that, as one patient said, 'People are pretty rotten, you can't trust anyone'. Love comes to be regarded as weakness. Behind this outer protective shell, they will secretly feel small, weak, helpless and afraid, just as they really did when they were tiny children in an unhelpful family life.

Our culture-pattern both expresses and also creates and maintains this state of affairs. It is essentially competitive. Everyone wants to be stronger or more successful than other people, because it does not seem safe not to be. Life is based on the fear that the weakest go to the wall, and this attitude is just as obviously true of socialist dictatorships as of capitalist democracies. From the external and material point of view everyone seems to be busy *defending material security,* as individuals, classes and nations, against those who are believed to be seeking to rob them of it (and who, because of the vicious circle this sets up, often are seeking to rob them of it, always in supposed self-defence). But this defence of our sheer *physical existence* masks a far more subtle problem, that of safeguarding the coherence, stability and value of our 'ego', our *existence as persons.* From the internal and psychological point of view everyone is busy *defending the integrity, independence and freedom of his own individual personality,* from the dangers that seem so convincingly omnipresent. Behind all

* *Sociology.* Oxford Univ. Press, 1934, p. 106.

this is the legacy of fear and weakness from childhood, and the deep-buried need for that 'Infantile Dependence' which Fairbairn held to be the cause of neurosis, and which everyone is concerned to deny even though in some degree it must survive in all of us.

In order to master and crush this dependent infant and prevent anyone seeing him, every active capacity, muscular, sexual, intellectual, practical, is made use of in aggressive ways. With some insecure people even their humour has to be aggressive because of their struggle to keep their end up. The whole situation is caricatured in what we have now come to call 'One-up-manship'. But human beings are not naturally antisocial, they become so when at heart they are afraid. One patient once said to me 'When I am very frightened I can only keep going at all by hating', and another came to the conclusion 'When I can get angry I feel I have plenty of energy and can do things. If not, I'm timid and daren't face people'. It is noticeable that the two opposite types who emphasize on the one hand bodily prowess and on the other intellectual ability, frequently adopt attitudes of contempt for each other, thus betraying a need to compensate for some secret felt lack or sense of inferiority, some deep fear of not being an adequate person.

All this can best be presented concretely in a particular case, of a man who was quite extraordinarily successful but suffered emotional tortures within himself. He said, 'A lot of my tiredness is boredom. We had friends in last night and by 11.30 p.m. I felt exhausted and wished they'd go. Then one of them started a really interesting conversation and I woke up. There are few people you can have meaningful conversations with. Interest has to be aroused by a person.' I commented, 'If no interest is aroused you can't live. If life itself wasn't made interesting to you as a child, you have a job to keep going.' He replied, 'I was bored all my childhood. My parents didn't really let me be interested in anything. They didn't stop me but they showed no interest in anything I did, or else criticized and depreciated it. Things came to seem not worth while. My boredom is a disease now. I've got into this pattern and can't get out of it. I was not encouraged to be interested in anything but business, and then only along father's lines. I wasn't allowed to ask real questions and was never told anything.' Here is a case of an environment which was not in any sense physically bad, but it was psychologically not only unnourishing but positively inhibiting, and it prevented the development of a self-assured and self-confident personality.

The results of this are seen in his further comments. 'I still don't like having anything to do with people, I'm frightened of them. I expect them to be hostile and critical. In fact, outwardly, I can get on well with them, but that doesn't alter how I feel. If I'm at all in the limelight I feel everyone is making fun of me. I feel no one's to be trusted. Look at all the laws we have defending everyone against everyone else. That's why I want to stop in bed, so that I don't get involved with people, though of course I don't. I don't expect to be able to pour oil on troubled waters. With hostile people you've got to be hostile back and so the pattern goes on. I don't *think* that that's true or sensible, I know it needn't work that way, but that's how I grew up to feel.' In point of fact at this stage he was already finding that as anxiety diminished and self-confidence grew, it was becoming more possible to move amongst people with quiet self-assurance, without suspicious or quarrelsome tendencies, and with an openness of nature that calls out trust, friendliness, and a sense of security in others.

Thus there has emerged the picture of *a more primitive level of disturbance than the moral level of the struggle against bad impulses; a level where we come upon the original and primary weakness and helplessness of the tiny infant who is completely at the mercy, not so much of what we may surmise to be his inherited nature, but of what we can often plainly see to be his unsatisfactory and uncomprehending environment.* One of the easy self-deceptions that adults often shelter behind is that babies are too small to know, to understand, to feel, and that one does not, therefore, have to try to understand the baby or to study his feelings, so long as he is physically well cared for. Meanwhile the baby can withdraw his vital natural self from his unhelpful or hurtful world and hide it away in his unconscious, while he develops a superficial self in consciousness which maintains a shallow and probably compliant relationship with parents and others which is enough to 'get by' with. Many a 'quiet good child' who causes no trouble, is already in this crippled state of personality, doomed to grow up with his 'true self' lost inside, or as Dr. D. W. Winnicott puts it, hidden away in cold storage awaiting a better chance to be reborn. The trouble is that the buried infant is the headquarters of undiminished secret fears in the personality, from which arises a constant secret pull to retreat from every stress. A patient capably running his own business once said to me: 'My first reaction to everything is to draw back and feel I can't cope. Then I have to stop myself and think "Yes I can" and bring myself forward again.'

In Chapter 4, we mentioned that the problem in depression is the disposal of aggression. If we let it out we hurt others and if we lock it in we hurt ourselves. What can we do with it? If aggression were in truth an inborn and unchangeable drive in itself, there would be no answer to that problem. If, however, aggressive feeling and behaviour arises against the background of deeper fear, against which it is an attempted defence, then the radical 'cure' of the problem of depression and of the aggressive impulses which play so large a part in it, is to be reached by going behind it to the basic fears which hold the personality in thrall.

We may mention that the commonest precipitating cause of the onset of depression is an experience of 'loss', especially the loss of a person who is important to us. The classic explanation of this was in terms of the guilt that is felt over having repressed unconscious destructive feelings against those we love. We must now, however, go further with this problem, in terms not of the 'guilt' aspect of depression but in terms of the 'apathy' that is so undermining a component of this illness. In fact, as Fairbairn pointed out, most patients do not use the term depression with particular reference to guilt-burdened experiences, but much more to denote the feelings of loss of interest and of energy, and of the sense of worthwhileness in living that sum up into a devitalized state of mind. The reason why such a reaction should occur over an experience of loss is clear. If a much loved person who has been a source of real support in life is suddenly taken away, the fear-ridden child in the deep unconscious feels lost and alone and takes refuge in profound mental withdrawal. People in a state of grief, whether normal or depressed, are 'shut in' with their private thoughts, are liable to lose contact with the real outer world, and with it to lose for the time being the incentives to living that keep our active capacities in being. *The problem of depression really runs back into this deeper problem of 'regression' or the mental withdrawnness that makes for loss of contact with real life.*

CHAPTER SEVEN

THE STRUGGLE TO ACHIEVE A REAL 'SELF'

IT was stated in the last chapter that when Freud's interest moved beyond instincts to the analysis of the 'Ego' or 'Personal Self', he really prepared the way for a psychology that should no longer be concerned with the fate of particular and separate 'impulses' as if they could exist as things-in-themselves but rather with the nature and state of the 'self' as a whole. Human nature is not an arena inside which things called instincts or impulses compete with one another. Each human being possesses unique individuality to some degree, and his human nature is that of a 'personal self' which finds expression in emotions and impulses, thoughts and actions, which are his own activities. The nature of our 'impulses' is determined by the state and quality of our total 'self' as well as by the nature of the objective situation we react to. If we have impulses which conflict with one another, that is a sign that our 'self' has to that extent lost its proper unity, as happens to a country in a state of civil war. We have become divided in and against ourselves, or in the jargon we are becoming used to nowadays we are 'split personalities'.

When a person is criticized as 'egotistical', i.e. over-concerned about his ego or *self*-centred, he is being blamed for the attention he is bestowing on his ego. Such criticism is entirely unrealistic. When our body is hurt, no one blames us for paying attention to it. We would be much more likely to be blamed for neglecting it. A wound must be healed, a hurt spot protected, an infection eliminated. But when the hurt has been sustained by the mental, instead of the bodily self, the all too prevalent attitude is 'Forget it' or 'Don't be so touchy'. Such impatient advice, it is true, is mostly given by people who want to have the privilege of blurting out whatever they think without having to consider others' feelings. But those who rather pride themselves on being tough usually hide a very sensitive self of their own behind the scenes in their mind, and do not wish to be reminded of it by seeing its manifestations occur in other folk. I am not, of course, advocating a sentimental coddling or pandering to either body or mind. I am calling attention to the fact that 'personalities' can be seriously hurt as well as bodies. Emotional damage can be done to the growing self in childhood, the effects of which will be felt for a lifetime, and will produce not hours but years of secret misery. A wound to a person's self-respect, whether malicious or careless, can start up buried problems which the sufferer may not have the capacity to solve. One of the greatest of the early analysts, Karl Abraham, tells of a male patient whose depression of psychotic intensity broke out when a mentally cruel school-teacher called him a 'physical and mental cripple' in front of the class. One sometimes hears the expression, 'So-and-so is silly to let herself be hurt so easily'. If such a remark were made about a person who winced bodily if a serious wound were accidentally touched on, the callousness of the critic would be obvious. We have just got to get used to the fact that wounds to the personality may be more serious and take far longer to heal than wounds to the body. Self-centredness is a symptom. The egotistical person is trying to carry on personal relationships while feeling persistent concern for the stability of his personality, and therewith for his capacity to cope with life. He is seeking recognition which will help him to keep his 'ego' functioning. It is true he no doubt needs friendly help to understand what he is doing and do it in ways that are not so irritating to those around him, but it is a very ignorant judgement that would dismiss him as merely conceited. Such a person has cause to be anxious about what we mean by 'I' or 'me'. Most likely all too little constructive attention was paid to him as a child and he never was able to feel of any real worth. He has felt ever since that his 'I' was in danger, has got to be safeguarded, defended, supported; and it is coming to be seen that this, rather than the 'control of impulses', is the key problem of human nature.

In the last chapter we were still thinking a good deal, if not wholly, from the point of view of different kinds of impulse, and we pointed out how psychoanalysis has moved its emphasis from sex to aggression, and is now in process of moving it once again on to fear, not the rational fears of adult life but the deep surviving fears of infancy. But this has led us naturally to take the further step of moving the emphasis away from 'impulses' and on to the 'self' to which they belong. It is far more usual than not to find human beings to some degree in a state of internal division as regards the very make-up of their personality. 'Split personality' is not confined to the very serious illness known as schizophrenia. It is all a matter of degree, and some degree of loss of wholeness or internal unity of the 'self' is universal. To put it another way, the completely integrated personality is only an ideal goal towards which we approximate. The degree to which any of us do so is primarily determined by how helpful our environment was in the all-important first few years.

In the simplest and broadest terms, we have already seen that *the pattern of this division in our total self is that of a strained and anxious adult trying to cope with the outer world while doing his best to suppress an inner self that is in a state of childlike, or even infantile, fear and dependent need.* How clearly this is sometimes felt can be seen from this dream of a capable middle-aged woman who had deliberately changed her profession and retrained for a different kind of work. She was finding the going hard and in one period of anxiety she dreamed: 'I was a lost little girl, crying and trying to find a father.' It is significant that in reality all through childhood she had been very conspicuously kept away from her father and had no real relationship with him. Thus she had grown up lacking the stabilizing and strengthening influence of a good father-daughter relationship, and under stress later in life felt like a lost little girl. That was repressed and she only became aware of it through a dream, but its effects were visible consciously as an anxiety state.

The position, then, is not that we have inherited 'lusts and passions of the flesh' which are hard to control and which resist all too successfully the civilizing process, nor even that we have out-of-date things called 'infantile fears' surviving in us from the past. The problem is that our personality development is arrested and uneven, that in part we are still frightened children, and that it is all too easy to prevent a child from growing up to be a mature and fully developed whole adult person. Our personality is complex and not by any means all on the same level. For example a person may appear to be intellectually brilliant and highly developed, and yet emotionally a child. This is not, however, a split into a 'thinking self' and a 'feeling self'; rather is it true that a person can use his intellect in a mature way so long as he is not in an emotionally disturbed state, but once his anxieties have been aroused he will use those same intellectual capacities in most unreasonable and prejudiced ways because he is now thinking like a frightened child. The division is always, whatever signs it throws out, that of a frightened child-self inside, feeling small, weak, inadequate, and unable to cope with life, and a conscious self of everyday living struggling to deal with life in the ways expected of adult people.

The importance of the arousal of strong fear at too early an age lies in the fact that it blocks the normal and natural processes of self-development. The non-anxious and undisturbed child is ongoing in his mental growth all the time. He develops in an active and self-confident way, trying out his powers in all kinds of experiments and making friendly approaches to people, since he has not experienced any reasons for holding back. His momentary hesitations and timidities in attempting some new thing as yet a bit beyond his powers, are overcome by trial and error. His momentary caution in meeting some quite new type of person is easily banished by a friendly attitude to him, because he has had no reason for suspecting that someone might not be friendly. Under such circumstances his nature will develop as an undivided whole, and when he is grown up he will not suffer from a neurosis. According to his innate temperament he may be more or less active, sensitive, and so on, but his personality will not display that chronic state of internal civil war, 'splitting' and conflict which leads to illness.

But how many children have such favourable circumstances in which to grow? It is easy to see what serious results may follow from growing up in a really bad home, where the child has to contend with neglect or violence, but distortion of personality can result from much less than that. Fear is the most dangerous of all emotions to arouse in a child. A sarcastic or critical father, a nagging and guilt-producing mother, will make a child grow up far more unsure of himself than anyone realizes. Parents frequently relieve their own anxieties and tension by shouting at the children, never heeding the look of fear on the child's face. How often have patients said to me something like this: 'My father or mother had a fixed idea of what sort of a person I ought to be, and there was always trouble because I couldn't fit into their pattern.' At a much earlier age two avoidable mistakes are fairly common to observe. Babies are still far too often left to cry themselves into states of terror, and the superficial excuse made, 'It's good for them to cry, they must exercise their lungs.' The second and even harder mistake to understand is that some parents do not seem to realize that a tiny baby needs to be talked to, needs to have a personal interest shown in him, needs to be helped to make the first steps in human relationships by responding to happy, playful sounds of parents' voices, and their smiles and caresses. The excuse is made that if you pay too much attention to the baby, you'll spoil him and he'll demand more and more. But if you deprive him of these vitamins of personality growth, you'll certainly spoil his chance to develop into a happily socialized, friendly and co-operative person.

The fact is that we cannot just see to it that the baby's bodily needs are met and leave his personality needs to chance. We cannot take for granted that the human infant will inevitably grow a whole, normally developed self. If he grows in an environment that is unresponsive to him, he is much more likely to grow into a most undermining feeling of emptiness and nonentity. The foundations of the personality are laid in the first year by the quality of the infant's relationships with first mother and then father: and though the mother has most to do with the infant, it is essential that the father should have a real relationship with the child from the start. We do not as yet know anything like as much as we want to know about these earliest stages of the growth of personality. What we do know is that the deeper down you go into the unconscious of very disturbed persons, the more you come upon a level of their mental life where they are dominated by fear and feel that they have hardly got a personality at all. At an astonishingly early age, the vital heart of the infant self can shrink away from a hurtful or neglectful outer world and turn inwards to bury itself in the secret hiding place of the unconscious, as if it felt it were returning back again into the womb for safety. In fact, phantasies and dreams which express the idea of an escape back into the womb are quite common. An example of this phantasy in a not very greatly disguised form in a dream is the following: 'I was walking along the street and suddenly I felt there was some great danger. Atom bombs were going to be dropped and I rushed down into an underground, private family shelter for safety.' But the phantasy often occurs without any disguise at all.

Total withdrawal, a complete breaking off from external relationships, would, naturally, result in such profound apathy that death would result. That is a possibility, but what usually happens is that the child withdraws his sensitivity from contact with the hurtful environment, and develops an interior life in part, while in part he maintains a more mechanical and unfeeling surface self with which to make the necessary adjustments to his outer world. The results of this become noticeable as he grows up, through absent-mindedness, preoccupation, and dwelling on phantasy. We say of this kind of person, 'He's miles away; when you speak to him he doesn't seem to hear or notice.' Such a person is physically present, you can touch him and engage him in conversation, but somehow you feel his mind is only half on the subject. Such persons will often complain under treatment of the great difficulty they have in keeping their attention fixed on anything. Their mind wanders away to their safe phantasy world inside, and in bad cases the only thing that attention can be really concentrated on is this secret phantasy life.

It follows that such a person is correspondingly out of touch with externally real things, fails to notice what everyone else sees, or to pick up information that most people gather almost unconsciously. The detached person, therefore, does not know his way around, is often at a loss to know how to behave or what to do in circumstances that present no difficulty to the person who is 'in touch' with life. Sometimes, as an alternative, the detached person is very well in touch with his environment in so far as it is a matter of information about impersonal things; but he does not 'know' human beings and may quite miscalculate what other people are thinking and feeling and how they will react. Withdrawn patients frequently say, 'I don't feel like a proper person; everyone else seems to know what they want, I never know. I don't seem to have a mind of my own.' A further consequence is the feeling of inferiority, of being at a disadvantage with other people, of always 'missing the bus' or 'being the odd man out'. A still more disturbing result is the inability to get really interested in anyone or anything, the inability to fall in love or even to form a genuine friendship, or to enthuse about things. As a defence against anxiety and loss of self-respect over these limitations, the attitude is often adopted of some measure of contempt for and superiority to more normal people who can 'get so stupidly worked up' about things of no real worth. Yet when the detached person asks himself 'What is of real worth?', he finds that he feels so little about anything that nothing seems to have much value.

When this inability to feel for one's outer world serves, as it is meant to do, as a defence against people, it may well lead to surprising callousness in the treatment of others. If you have to keep people at arm's length because of deep and largely unconscious fears of them, you cannot know if or when you have hurt their feelings, and you tend to become insensitive in personal relationships. What is morally criticized as 'selfishness' is often not so much a greedy, grasping acquisitiveness, as a type of behaviour based on the failure to take other people into account emotionally at all. The 'self who can feel' is missing from the 'self who behaves in the social setting'. But the missing real self who could 'feel' is missing because long ago he withdrew in fear and he cannot now easily get back in touch with the world outside himself. A patient who was very disturbed at a prospective visit from an overbearing in-law, came one day in a markedly shut-in state of mind and said: 'I'm frightened of her, and I seem to be going farther and farther away in my mind. I'm afraid I'll get so far away I won't be able to get back again.' In fact, when a profound withdrawal has taken place very early in life, it is extremely difficult to get this 'lost self' back in touch again. It is not for nothing that the idea of a rebirth has played such a large part in religious thought, for, under deep analytic treatment, patients nearly always resort periodically to birth symbolism and dreams of having a baby, when they are busy with their deep need to get their 'lost self' restored to practical life once more. One patient expressed her sense of tremendous difficulty about achieving this, in a dream of watching at a childbirth. The infant's head appeared and then it stuck fast, and though tremendous efforts were made to drag it out by sheer force, it could not be moved. The implication is that the frightened withdrawn hidden heart of the personality *cannot* be *forced* back into life; but if the person is made to feel really secure, then the withdrawn part of the personality will begin to re-emerge, if somewhat cautiously and slowly for a long time. A male patient dreamed of a baby in the process of birth wondering whether to go on coming out or to go back in, a dream which shows clearly how the total self can be in a state of conflict between the developmental urge forwards and a deep fear-created longing to escape backwards again.

This 'pull backwards' is what lies behind the passive forms or aspects of nervous illness sometimes called 'exhaustion neurosis', and in general summed up in the comprehensive term 'Regression'. The struggling adult is seeking to 'progress' in face of the powerful undermining backward pull of the frightened child within who is seeking to take flight from life; and the result may well be an involuntary breakdown into some form of regressive illness. It is not, therefore, to be wondered at that this psychological condition of the personality sets up very great tension within both body and mind. Persistent and unrelieved tension is today one of the most menacing and widespread forms of illness, or rather we ought to say that it is the ultimate cause of that ever-enlarging group of illnesses now known as psychosomatic. If our infancy and childhood has left us in this unhappy state of the divided self, with the vital heart of selfhood locked away in an undeveloped condition, then living is like going out to shop having left most of one's money at home. To use a much more accurate simile, facing adult life is like being a small child forced by unkind circumstance to be the 'little mother' and shoulder responsibilities that only a fully developed adult can bear without harm and exhaustion.

Naturally, therefore, we find the most intense efforts being made by people to 'pull themselves together' and force themselves to prove adequate to the demands of life. It is surprising how often patients will say, 'I was a timid, shy little thing' or 'I was a cry-baby', or in one case 'I was a miserable little worm up to the age of ten, and then I suddenly realized that I couldn't go on like that and I made a terrific effort to pull myself out of it.' There are a number of ways in which that can be done. One is to aim at the compromise which we nowadays call 'Brinksmanship'. If one is afraid to be too closely involved with people and also afraid of too drastic a retreat into isolation and loneliness, then one can try to maintain a 'half in and half out' position. Relationships can be superficially carried on with every appearance of normality and yet no real depth of feeling is experienced. As one patient put it, 'I'm a chronic non-joiner. I live in a state of muted feeling, on the edge of life, and I can't put myself fully into anything.' Yet to all appearance she lived quite an active social life. If this middle position of compromise cannot be maintained emotionally, then one finds a drift either into physical symptoms to relieve dammed up tensions, or else into that distressing oscillation of moods between being 'the life and soul of the party' when with people and depressed or apathetic when alone.

One method of trying to solve the problem of the frightened child within is of particular importance, and is bound up with our cruel cultural attitudes of contempt for weakness. A patient once told me that he had seen a film in which a Major was castigating himself for what he called his 'cowardice', his liability to feel fear in face of danger. One not seldom finds that the fear of fear is greater than the fear of danger, and in this film the Major in question must have had a sudden flash of real insight when he remarked: 'Ah! I suspect that there is a crippled child somewhere inside all of us.' The obviously correct treatment for a crippled and frightened child, wherever it is to be found, is to meet it with sympathetic understanding and protective help. But if this undermined child is a part of our own make-up, we are most likely to have been taught to treat him without much mercy. When the child is still quite small he is likely to have been told, 'Don't be a silly little cry-baby' and every effort will have been made to 'toughen him up'. Nobody asks what is happening to his fear and distress which he is being forced to hide from disapproving grown-ups. The argument may even be used that he will presently find the world a hard place and he had better get used to it early. The fact is that the more he is protected from fear at an early age, the stronger he will be when the time comes later on to face the complex adult world. *Premature toughening is no sound substitute for the growth of a genuine basic feeling of security which gives inner strength,* but what it does do is to make the child grow up more vulnerable than ever by dividing him against himself and preventing the resolution of his early fears. If he is by nature an energetic or an intellectually gifted child, he will gradually find ways of exploiting his trump cards of natural ability, and will build up, by methods which are admiringly called 'self-discipline' and 'laudable ambition' and 'not sparing himself', a secondary personality capable of coping with competitive conditions in the adult world. This may be based on either a predominantly compliant or an aggressive attitude, with many modifications and disguises. He may very well achieve outstanding success in material and social ways if he has real ability, but nobody, for a long time not even himself, knows the price he is paying. Characteristics of aggressiveness or restless over-activity betray the presence of inner tension which is always needing release. In course of time he may begin to realize that he is a bad relaxer, indeed that he cannot relax at all, that he cannot even go to sleep at night but tosses about or lies awake 'thinking' about things that would be better left alone till next day arrives: or if he does sleep, then he must keep restlessly active by dreaming hard a lot of the night. Presently maybe a duodenal ulcer or headaches or some other variety of personality tension worked out through the body appears. Then, just as he has attained the height of his ambition, he usually 'breaks down from overwork'.

Bodily and mental tension and the inability to relax are perhaps the most widely spread of all signs today of disharmony within the personality. Because in such a state genuine growth towards maturity is impossible, one finds that the unhappy person concerned is very likely to have grown more rigid and unadaptable as time has passed, and to have become not a more human being but a high-powered routine of business activity. The wife of one such man said: 'My husband works all the time. He does nothing else. He is only a lodger in the house.' Going along with that there is usually plenty of irritability and general bad temper, as the strain of living comes to be felt more and more, and yet the patient cannot alter his ways just by trying to. He seems to be in the grip of a secret slave-driver within himself who gives him no peace or rest. It is astonishing how much sheer self-hatred can be found in the mental make-up of such a person. The basis of this hostility to self, or rather to the weakened child within, is the fear of weakness, and the sense of humiliation at feeling a need to depend on another person for the solving of a problem in the personality, once one is grown up. As was very simply and pointedly said to me: 'Your independent personality comes up and you want to do things on your own.'

This is the source of the greatest difficulty in treatment. One of Freud's most important discoveries was that patients *resist* the very treatment they seek. One male patient, in a phase when he was being quietly independent and only superficially co-operative with me, dreamed that he was in the patient's chair in my room and wanting to relax and rest; then he found another version of himself standing behind the chair and looking down on him with hate and hostility, and with a dagger to attack him. He was hating the part of himself that needed my help, and so, though only showing it in a very mild way, he was hating and resisting me for being the person whose help he needed. Many a husband or wife similarly becomes irritable with the marriage partner because of an unconscious fear of being too dependent. A more extreme example is that of a patient who, in an extremely ill and terrified state, screamed at me: 'You want me to come creeping and crawling to you for help, but I'll damn well show you.' In fact, of course, what I above all wanted was to help her to become unafraid so that she did not feel as if she were creeping and crawling in feeling normal human needs.

The patient's determination to save himself by his own methods, which turn out to be methods of self-exhaustion, can sometimes frustrate treatment entirely. This is beautifully illustrated by the following account given to me by one man of his car driving. He said: 'When I'm driving my car, I am obsessed with the fear that the petrol will run out. I know it won't but that doesn't stop me having this compelling fear that it will. I am calculating all the time how much I have left and how far it is to the next garage. Of course, I know that the best way to conserve petrol is to drive at a moderate speed and not vary it, but I can't do that. The lower I see my petrol getting, the faster I drive. It is a compulsion.' What he was really talking about was not his car and his petrol, but his 'self' and his 'energy'. This is the story of most breakdowns of over-active people, whether they are driving themselves in a hectic social round or in overwork. Behind all that, lie their deep hidden fears of inadequacy going back to infancy. Their drive is a gallant if misguided effort to achieve a viable personality, to get to feel like a real 'somebody' in the absence of that basic security and inner strength which every human being should be enabled to grow in the first few years of life.

It is a sad thing to contemplate how many people are living only half a life. They have far richer potential powers than they have ever been mentally free enough to make use of. That is what really accounts for much of the discontent which is so widely felt. No social or economic betterment can cure this problem. It makes one realize how deep and difficult is the task of psychotherapy. In its most radical form, it is nothing less than the rebirth and regrowth of the 'true self'. How far this is possible in later life will be a problem we shall consider in Part 3. Whereas in past ages it would seem that widespread mental disturbance mostly took the forms of guilt and depression, it appears to me that psychoanalysis is following slowly in the wake of a change in public reaction on this matter. Perhaps with the decline of hell-fire preaching, and the lessening of religious emphasis on the negative themes of sin, repentance and judgement, in favour of more positive preaching, and with the increase of 'freethinking' and of the scientific or impersonal approach, leading to widespread uncertainty about all 'values', it has become much harder for individuals to make the 'moral diagnosis' of disturbed personality problems in themselves or to use it as a defensive method of trying to crush down their conflicts. That is to the advantage of true morality which becomes more free to present itself in terms of positive and constructive values, the less it is used as a whip to flog anxious and fear-ridden minds. But the result in general is that our literary analysers of the mental life of our time more and more concentrate on the description of feelings of futility, meaninglessness, and inability to find life worthwhile. Perhaps the most revealing catchword of our age is 'I couldn't care less', i.e. the defence of feeling nothing at all.

In *The Catcher in the Rye* J. D. Salinger, for example, tells the story of an adolescent youth of sixteen years who has obvious ability but no interest capable of making life mean anything worthwhile to him. He drifts through a series of pointless activities, trying all the time to get some real experience, and ending every time in failure and disillusionment. He exhibits the typical detachment and inability of the withdrawn or schizoid person simply to enter into something and enjoy it. He has to stand outside everything he does and watch it in a critically rejective way. Thus he was watching a very good roller-skater on the stage but he says, 'I couldn't enjoy it because I kept picturing him *practising* to be a guy that roller-skates on the stage. It seemed so stupid.'*

An even more morbid and tragic account of the schizoid personality who is totally cut off from any meaningful living, and merely exists in apathy, is to be found in *Waiting for Godot* by Samuel Beckett. I believe that these writers are making an accurate study of the real cause of mental ill-health in their descriptions of the failure of interest and constructive activity and meaningful living in emotionally withdrawn people, which is far more prevalent

* Pelican, p. 143.

today than feelings of guilt. It is usually masked and hidden by superficial social adjustments, and the necessity to carry on the activities prescribed for keeping life going. But when we get behind the scenes of this surface life, we find that many people are getting astonishingly little deep satisfaction out of living. This is not a criticism but a diagnosis. We have to face the fact that there is a terrible failure, in this age of 'scientific progress', to enable children to grow up with a whole and undivided and healthy personality in which all their resources of energy and feeling are freely available to live by.

CHAPTER EIGHT

THE BASIC CONFLICT IN THE PERSONALITY

OUR argument so far has brought us to the conclusion that psychodynamic research has shifted the emphasis, so far as the ultimate cause of mental ill-health is concerned, away from the problems of moral conflict and the struggle to control antisocial impulses, on to the problems of the struggle of a personality already emotionally damaged and weakened in early childhood, to keep functioning on an adult level and cope with the demands of life without breakdown. The fear that dominates and conditions all other fears is the fear of breaking down as a person, becoming unable to carry adequately the responsibilities of grown-up living.

There can be very few human beings who do not know what it is like to feel inadequate in face of some important task with which life confronts them. There are all too many people who experience in varying degrees the more radical and frightening sense of inadequacy to life as a whole. One patient who ultimately worked right through a long analysis to the achievement of physical health, an independent professional career, and finally marriage, said at one point: 'Fear is the trouble. I'm afraid of everything. I'm afraid of life itself.' I have already stressed the fact that the older moral diagnosis regarded our undisciplined instinctive strength as the cause of mental ill-health. Present-day psychodynamic research is attributing it rather to the undermining effects within the physically and intellectually grown-up personality of fear and ego-weakness persisting from early childhood.

Morality remains a problem on the level of the social and legal management of our human relationships in those co-operative activities that make up community living: and also in the formulation of ethical, humanistic and religious ideals of living. But we descend to a more primitive, premoral level of human experience when we deal with the root causes of mental illness. The tragic plight of the mentally ill person is that he struggles, and usually has struggled for years, to conduct his life in the generally accepted mature and responsible ways, while he does not possess the psychic equipment needed for this purpose. While he is forcing himself along day by day to do his duties and to accept other people's dependencies on him, deep in his unconscious experience of life he feels to be a small, weak, frightened child desperately in need of someone he can depend on to find security and the chance to regrow his personality.

In psychotherapy, one constantly comes on the phenomenon of a patient feeling that he has somehow lost a vital part of his essential self; that all his energy and emotional capacity is not available for use. Dr. Winnicott suggests that when the parental environment does not adequately nourish a baby's proper and natural self, the infant puts his 'true self' into cold storage until such time as he can find conditions proper to its growth; in its place he develops a 'false self on a compliance basis' with which he can get by in dealing with the external world. This sense of part of the self being locked away inside out of use, is a quite definite experience which many patients come upon as they get deeper into the analysis of their personality. It carries with it the feeling of lack of genuine self-realization, of only living a partial and unfulfilled life, of having undiscovered potentialities. Along with this there usually goes a sadness and feeling of frustration and disillusionment, and even of futility in life.

Thus one woman said: 'I love my husband, but when I want to show my feelings, the feeling doesn't come. I feel I've lost part of myself and I don't know where to find it.' Another patient whose work involved writing said: 'I sit for half an hour staring with increasing resentment at the blank sheet of paper and can't think of an idea. I get angry with myself and say, "It's ridiculous. You with a University education and you can't think of a thing to say". But that only makes it worse.' That this was not an inherent inability was clear from the fact that at other times he could feel suddenly mentally released, ideas would then flow freely and he would lose himself in his work. Yet another woman said: 'People think I'm lucky. I have a kind husband and money, and I could do anything I want to do, but I just do not know what I want to do. If you said to me: "Here's a completely free day in which you can do as you like", I would not be able to think what to do. I've no real interests. I don't feel really alive. I feel I've wasted my life.' This woman was University trained and had a first class intelligence. Nevertheless, the vital heart of her personality from which spontaneous interest and really meaningful activity might flow, seemed shut away. It was not that she was idle. In fact her days were a hectic rush of activities of a kind that had to be got through. She raced from one thing to another, yet found no significance and no satisfaction in anything she did. It was in reality a frantic attempt to persuade herself that she had got interests, and all the while she knew that it meant little to her.

It is not, then, surprising that such forced activity repeatedly broke down into exhaustion and depression. This is a far more common condition than is recognized. A great deal of what looks superficially like a tremendous zest for living is a defence against an apathy and lack of true feeling within, which is too frightening to face.

Our culture makes people feel ashamed of any sign of weakness in the personality, as if it were a personal fault. Thus, every attempt is made to hide it and deny it, while a forced half-alive existence is carried on over the top of a repressed part of the personality which remains in serious need of help. We need make no secret of ills of the body and most people are quite eager to discuss them. But the attitude of Samuel Butler's *Erewhon,* where all illness was treated as a thing to be ashamed of and to be hidden, is by us applied to ills of the mind. Certainly nowadays we freely discuss the widespread incidence of neurosis, but that is impersonal and tacitly assumes that there is plenty of neurosis about somewhere but not in us. This attitude is symptomatic of the basic conflict in human nature in our culture.

Dr. Ian Suttie in *The Origins of Love and Hate,* said that there is 'a taboo on tenderness' in our civilization, which favours tough, competitive, aggressive characteristics, the hard thrustful type who will ride roughshod over others to achieve success, the unscrupulous type who regards it as clever to outwit rivals in the game of grab. These are the ideals of a neurotic society, of the culture of a world built on fear. This 'taboo on tenderness' is a defence against the underlying 'fear of weakness'. The fundamental taboo in our culture is on the admission of weakness, and such a culture is doomed to be quite incapable of solving the problem of mental ill-health. Whatever else it achieves by way of scientific mastery of physical nature and economic accumulation of wealth, it will not achieve *mens sana in corpore sano.* Only a culture that learns to respect and understand human personality for its own sake, and be as patient and helpful to personality-weakness as to physical weakness will be capable of solving the problems of mental ill-health.

The basic conflict in the sick mind is the struggle to deny, fight down and master a weak and frightened child within. This comes out often with quite astonishing clarity in psychoanalytic investigation. Perhaps the clearest and simplest expression of the internal battle I have come across was in the dream of a young middle-aged married woman. She had had a more than usually hurtful childhood in a home where drink, poverty and a large family left little security for anyone. Through a long psychoanalytic treatment she maintained a distinctly hostile attitude. She openly disliked and hated me for a long time, and as this diminished it was replaced by a cold, aloof independence which made it extremely difficult to carry on the treatment. She was afraid to accept help, would repeatedly say she had never had anyone she could trust, anyone who had really understood her, and she had always had to manage alone. Gradually the fact emerged that she was actually afraid that if she did seek help from anyone, she would begin to make such big demands that they would soon grow tired of her and push her off. She was certain that would be my reaction. This, however, was the beginning of her recognition that a hidden part of herself, which had been so extensively denied the normal securities and affections of childhood, was still in a state of frantic anxiety, insecurity and loneliness, and felt utterly unable to face life.

At that point she had the following dream: 'I was a very anxious small girl, and I was standing at the door of a large room. I saw you sitting in a big armchair in the centre and I thought "If I could only get to him, I'd be safe". I ran across the room to you, but at once another little girl of the same age (obviously the other part of herself) walked quickly up in a cool, calm and collected way and got between me and you and pushed me back to the door again.' Here is her independent self feeling that at all costs she must manage alone and not let herself find any help in me. The result of that dream policy was seen in the next two years of suffering and struggle, in which she kept coming to sessions with me but was quite unable to let the frightened child within have the emotional protection and understanding she needed. In this case, the long struggle was finally cut short by a sudden 'breakdown', involuntarily, into a state of terrified helplessness and compulsive crying while all the fears of her childhood rushed back to consciousness. This proved a turning point, however, enabling her to make steady progress, while her whole personality became calmer, more friendly and more natural.

This part of the personality that conducts such a vicious campaign of self-persecution must, in fact, be itself understood and respected if it is to be outgrown. It develops out of the child's struggle to help himself when no one else is available to help. It is, of course, based on fear, the fear of failing to accomplish the task of growing up, the fear of appearing weak and a failure in the eyes of others, the fear of being at a disadvantage in the struggle with competitors. We may say that it has laudable aims, but they are defined exclusively in terms of anxiety and use the wrong methods of self-management; methods which prove to be self-destructive in the end, and lead the way to the very breakdown they seek to stave off. Yet it is difficult to see in what other way an anxious child could set about trying to cope with life in the absence of help. Fairbairn called this part of the personality 'the internal saboteur', and we shall later have to consider more closely, when we turn to 'Psychotherapy', how this saboteur receives far too much support from our cultural ideals.

Meanwhile we have to recognize in it the source of all that part of the strain and tension of mental illness which is purely internally caused. By contrast, there is plenty of strain and tension generated by the pressure of the external environment on a person who feels too nervous and basically timid to face it. But this strain is capable of being lived with. It is not so much 'fear' as 'fear of fear' that breaks people down. It is possible for an anxious person to face life quite consciously accepting the fact that he feels afraid; as if he were saying to himself, 'I know that I feel afraid and inadequate to this thing that I have to face. I always do and always have done, but nevertheless I can still carry my fear with me, and encourage myself with the knowledge that I always manage to cope and I will now.' That allows the frightened child in the unconscious to feel as if he were taken by the hand and helped on. Instead of living in an internal atmosphere of disintegrating self-hate, a reasonably supportive atmosphere makes slow but sure growth in self-confidence possible.

What breaks people down is the overplus of tension arising out of the 'fear of fear'. It compels a person to live constantly in a state of looking ahead with anxious foreboding, expecting the worst, doubling his initial fears, and developing chronic attitudes of self-contempt, self-hate and secret internal self-persecution as if he were his own internal slave-driver. Such people are afraid to let themselves be helped and this is the ultimate source of the 'resistance to treatment' which Freud discovered in every patient. Patients nearly always feel secretly ashamed of needing to be helped for something to do with their personality, and for a long time feel that any interpretation of their problems is criticism. We shall have to consider this more fully when we turn to the problems of 'Treatment'.

Meanwhile the self-destructiveness with which a human being can turn against himself can become so intense and can exert such frightening pressure on the 'self' from within, that quite frantic states of mind can develop. Psychoanalysis has long regarded 'masochism' as one of the major psychological problems. It is usually regarded as basically a phenomenon of sexual passivity and submissiveness to assault, bodily or mental. It is said that the masochist finds pleasure in suffering. Masochism can certainly take a sexual form, but I do not believe this is the true key to its understanding. I do not believe that any human being literally 'takes pleasure in suffering' as such. When an appearance of doing so is found, the interpretation is more subtle. What is certainly true is that human beings can and do enjoy 'exercising power', over other people if they can, and over themselves if there is no one else they can dominate. This gives them an illusory sense of being strong and counterbalances their fear of weakness at a deep level. I have often listened to patients cursing and vilifying themselves with fierce gusto. They obviously found pleasure in this fierce self-attack in so far as they were the 'strong' persons initiating it. But it is an illusion to think that in so far as they were also the persons suffering this attack they found pleasure in that. There is nothing pleasant about suffering *per se*, and pleasure only comes to be associated with it if the sufferer can find some reason in it, either in the infliction of it or the enduring of it, which enables him to feel he is overcoming his basic weakness. I once had a patient who, when she got frightened, would get angry and punch herself. When I remarked: 'You must be frightened being hit like that', she replied, 'I'm not being hit, I'm the one doing the hitting.' This was her way of trying to cancel out her fear. I used to notice how she would work herself up into a more and more intense and uncontrolled state until I intervened, and this is what happens when a secret internal self-attack is carried on in the hope of thereby mastering fear. If this process runs away with the patient and gets out of hand, he can drive himself into terror states of psychotic intensity. Every analyst and therapist will have seen this occur in sado-masochistic phantasies and dreams.

So far as my experience goes, the main task of psychoanalysis is to investigate, in a sympathetic way, this dangerously misguided attempt to deny weakness and force the personality to overreach its real strength. In proportion as this is successful in helping the patient to let himself be helped, an outgrowing of his neurosis becomes possible. This is therefore the point to turn to the question of treatment.

A passage from the consideration of theory to the study of treatment may be made via a quotation from Dr. H. V. Dicks. In an article on 'Object Relations Theory and Marital Studies'* he writes:

'Marriage is the nearest adult equivalent to the original parent-child relationship. Thus its success must revolve round the

* *Brit. J. Med. Psychol.* Vol. 37 Pt. 2, 1963, p. 129.

freedom to regress. The freedom to bring into the adult relation the deepest elements of infantile object-relations is a condition of growth. To be able to regress to mutual child-like dependence . . . without censure or loss of dignity, in the security of knowing that the partner accepts because he or she can . . . tolerate as a good parent this "little needy ego" when it peeps out—this is the promise people seek when they search for the one person who will be unconditionally loving, permissive and strong. . . . The search for this in heterosexuality determines the persistence with which people seek their "ideal mate".'

This gives us the key to the nature of psychotherapy. It is the search, not for the 'ideal mate' but for the 'ideal parent-substitute' who will do for the 'little needy child' inside the adult what the actual parents failed to do at the right time. One may say that the relationship between the psychoanalytical therapist and the patient lies midway between the parent-child relation and the husband-wife relation. It is not a relation between an actual parent and an actual child, nor is it a relation between two adults on terms of equality. It is a relation between the unhappy and undermined child in the adult patient and a therapist whose own 'internal child' ought to have been taken care of by his own training analysis so that he is free to be the stable adult parent-substitute to the lonely 'little needy child' in the patient. Only this kind of therapy can promote regrowth of personality from the depths, and, as Dicks says, 'its success must revolve around the freedom to regress . . . without censure or loss of dignity' in order to find the level of personality from which redevelopment can commence.

PART 3

TREATMENT

CHAPTER NINE

DIFFERENT LEVELS OF TREATMENT

---

1. *Types of Mental Illness*

I LISTENED recently to a broadcast appeal for funds for research on mental health. The broadcaster spoke of the very widespread suffering caused by mental illness, and then went on to say that some progress was being made by research workers on this problem. By way of illustration he mentioned one or two cases of small quantities of some obscure chemical substance having been found to produce mental illness. That was all. So far as this speaker was concerned the entire problem of the cause and cure of mental illness was confined to a purely physical, chemical factor. Such a broadcast as this, however well meant, is a gross misleading of public opinion. It is moreover, quite astonishing that anyone could find it possible to ignore the fact that there is a primary mental factor in mental ill-health. One has only to consider objectively the stories of real and heart-rending cruelty suffered by some patients in childhood, the stories of loveless and hate-filled homes, of cold and rejective homes; or to turn to the many tragic stories that can be told by the N.S.P.C.C., or by any Child Care Officer or Probation Officer, to see at a glance that the causes of mental illness cannot possibly be confined to the action of some chemical substances or to any purely physical or organic causes.

That is not to say that there is *no* place for physical and biological research on mental illness. Of course there is. If there is any chemical substance in food, or any genetic factor in biological inheritance that adversely affects mental stability, we must find out all that we can about it. Even to common observation and knowledge, chemical substances, as for example alcohol and opium, can have most disturbing effects on mental functioning: and if these, why not others? But it would be sheer blindness and materialistic prejudice to hold that physical factors cover the whole problem.

A clear example of the unsatisfactory way in which this question is sometimes handled in the popular press, is provided by an article in *The People,* for Sunday, February 3, 1963, by a Dr. Goodenough. After referring to the fact that 50 per cent of hospital beds are occupied by persons suffering from mental trouble, he goes on to say:

'Suddenly there has come a ray of hope. Such remarkable results have been achieved by the use of new drugs that soon these beds may be emptied in hundreds. Men and women suffering from anxiety and depression will no longer need weeks of nursing treatment. A regular dose of these drugs and they can be kept as happy and useful as the rest of us. And it could mean good-bye to the psychoanalyst's couch and the months of probing into the subconscious minds of rich neurotic patients. . . . The pill is better than the pep talk.' 'I am delighted to say that psychiatrists have discovered that I was right. The result is these remarkable cures of mental patients simply by using pills. No more long sessions on the psychiatrist's couch, talking about how they loved their mother and hated their father. Just a few pills a day and they are as happy as Larry.'

It would be hard to find a more unsatisfactory statement. We must allow for the fact that the article did not pretend to be a scientific one, but an obviously propagandist article in a popular newspaper. Nevertheless, it addresses the public on a matter of tremendous social importance, and it is a scientific subject. Thus we have the right to expect accuracy in the light of the evidence, and not propaganda. The attitude 'I was right' is not that of the scientist concerned only with truth, nor are we given truth. Thus psychotherapy is emphatically not a pep talk. 'These remarkable cures . . . by the use of new drugs' must be tested in the light of facts. In every mental hospital will be found a majority of patients who have had the advantage of the latest drugs over a long period, and for whom quite a number of these drugs have been tried with little result. I have had patients say to me, 'These drugs tide you over a crisis but they don't make any real difference in the end.' Dr. Goodenough cites a new drug known for short as M.A.O.I. as a real miracle-worker, but he has to add, 'We must be reasonable and cautious. Not all kinds of mental trouble can yet be cured by M.A.O.I. or by any other chemical. But we are on our way . . . and I believe that new drugs will soon be discovered to treat the brains of patients with other kinds of mental disorders'. A G.P. commented to me, 'This kind of article makes our patients come and demand to be given "the new drug". M.A.O.I. has been out a good five years now and medical men are quietly putting it in its proper place.' So, actually, we are only dealing with this doctor's personal belief as to what may one day be true, coupled with his rather obvious prejudice against psychotherapy. He cites a case where absorbing too much mineral copper from food was the cause of a curable mental disorder. That is not properly speaking a 'mental illness' except in a secondary and accidental sense. For every one such case, there are thousands who are ill through absorbing into their minds too much family hate, too little love, and too much misunderstanding of the child's needs in human relationship. This doctor thinks only in terms of treating the brain, as relieving the patients of the need to talk out their personal troubles in family and other settings. But that is not how many patients view the matter. They will say: 'This is the first time I have found anyone who would listen to me with understanding, and help me to come to terms with all the unhappiness in my life.' One other point must be noted. Dr. Goodenough says: 'A regular dose of these drugs and they can be kept happy, etc.' So after all, no fundamental difference has been made to the personality, the patient is no better or stronger or basically less anxious than before; only he is permanently dependent on drug taking. I have found that that is a situation that many patients simply refuse to accept. They will make use of a valuable drug in a crisis, but will refuse to go on in a state of permanent dependency on it, and do not give up their hope of something approaching a more radical change in their personality. It would be folly not to recognize the value of drugs in their proper place, but there is nothing whatsoever to be said for the putting forward of drugs as the final wonder cure to the exclusion of all attempts to understand the patient's personality.

The problem of mental health and ill-health is complex, and at least three different and distinct sets of facts must be taken into account, the physical, the social and the psychological; and these, in fact, constitute three different levels of approach to and treatment of personality problems. The question 'Is there a "cure" for mental illness?' turns rather into the more relevant question, 'What kind and degree of "cure" shall we aim at?' Just as there are different factors involved in the illness, so there are different methods of treatment, and different kinds of results are produced. These ought to be resorted to, not indiscriminately, but with understanding of what is involved, and *ultimately it is for the patient to decide what he really wants.*

It is useless to suggest psychoanalysis for a patient who is too acutely confused or distressed to co-operate in it, or for any other reason not likely to be able to make good use of it. Nor is it good to press drugs or electro-convulsive therapy on a very independent patient who fears becoming dependent on drugs or has a rooted objection to 'having anything done to his brain'. *In this field, above all the patient's personality must not be overridden.* It will not do for a doctor who is prejudiced against psychoanalysis to give advice against it to a type of patient who could really utilize it, nor does it do to 'send a patient for analysis' if he does not really want it. Those who make the most of this kind of treatment are those who freely and intelligently come to it of their own accord.

In a chapter on treatment in *You and Your Nerves*, I made three comments on the problem in general, and described three levels of treatment. I will here simply repeat those points without their original elaboration, and with but slight additional comment, as a starting-point for our present enquiry. The three comments were as follows: (i) In mental illness, 'it is no use asking questions about treatment, until we understand what it is that needs treating'. I will only add that I do not think it is necessarily a good thing for a patient to have a lot of detailed psychological knowledge. That usually has the effect of tempting him to try to keep his disturbed feelings repressed by turning the treatment into a purely intellectual discussion of his problems. Psycho-therapy is not the same thing as theorizing. But it is valuable for a patient to have a broad and sound knowledge of what is meant by 'disturbed personality' and of the way it causes physical upsets. I have sought in Parts 1 and 2 to give this knowledge in a simplified presentation of the theoretical issues involved at this stage of our understanding: just as in *You and Your Nerves* I gave a simpli-fied description of mental illness more from the point of view of its clinical symptoms. What is more important than intellectual knowledge, where treatment is concerned, is a capacity for insight, which varies greatly from one person to another. One patient came for psychoanalytical treatment on the advice of her physician but against the wishes of her parents: but she herself said, 'I have always felt this was the kind of treatment I needed'. She was in a seriously ill condition and after four years of analysis, every physi-cal symptom had disappeared. She said: 'I have never been so well in my life physically, but I've never been so unhappy'. This meant that she was now facing for the first time, and undisguised, the frustrations and fears that had made her ill. Nevertheless, over the ensuing ten years, she has never had a relapse into the old physical illnesses. Such an example shows how important it is for the patient to have some clear idea of the meaning of both the illness and the treatment.

(ii) The second comment was that 'a few talks or the reading of a book cannot of itself produce a cure'. They can, however, help to the right mental attitude to the problem.

(iii) The third comment was that 'in answer to the question "What can I do to get well?", we must put aside the idea of some simple prescription that will do the trick'. It is useless to raise false hopes of non-existent quick and easy cures. I recently read a publisher's advertisement for a book concerning Mr. So-and-So's 'cure for nerves in six sessions; no long psychoanalysis'. No doubt, if such a cure really existed, Mr. So-and-So would not be the only person to know about it, nor would there be so many people suffering from nerves unhelped. This field is wide open to the quack, and only reliable knowledge can be a safeguard. It is best, then, to discuss soberly the various possibilities, physical, social and mental, of treatment of neurosis, and what can be expected from them.

Leaving on one side organic diseases like disseminated sclerosis and Parkinson's disease, as purely physical, the illnesses we are concerned with can be grouped in various ways. The *psycho-neuroses* include obsessions, hysteric conditions, anxiety-states and phobic-states, while the more serious *psychoses* comprise the schizophrenias, manic-depressive states and paranoid conditions. This, however, is not a classification that is particularly helpful in deciding on treatment. Thus the eminent American psychiatrist, Dr. Harry Stack Sullivan, clearly divided the schizophrenias into organic and psychogenic conditions. In that case purely physical treatments would be appropriate to the organic illnesses, and psychotherapy to the psychogenic. Opinion differs. Many psychiatrists hold that all psychoses are basically organic diseases. On the other hand, other psychiatrists have found, along with psychoanalysts, that there are schizophrenic conditions which are accessible to, and can be influenced by, psychotherapy.

Manic-depressive states are usually divided into endogenous and reactive. *Endogenous*, i.e. literally 'growing from within', is a term that represents the manic-depressive problem as arising out of innate, hereditary, biological factors. If this be true, or in whatever cases it is true, the illness is purely organic and open only to physical treatments. *Reactive*, i.e. arising as an emotional reaction to some environmental situation (as when depression is brought on by bereavement), implies a psychodynamic rather than a purely biological view of the illness, and involves the relevance of psychotherapy. I have had a patient who, twelve years before he came for analysis, was diagnosed as constitutionally and incurably manic-depressive, and told that all that could be done was to control the condition by drugs. Drugs, however, failed to control the condition, but five years of psychoanalysis thoroughly eradicated his extreme, chronic, and debilitating mood swings.

Let us concede, then, that there is an as yet not accurately determined area or type of psychotic illness where the case is purely organic, possibly hereditary. Such cases would be primarily physical diseases with only secondary mental effects, and so do not concern us here. There remain large numbers of psychotic illnesses where the causes are psychological. I have no doubt that this will be more specifically proved as our knowledge of the failures of infantile ego-development increases. These are properly called 'mental illnesses'.

The psychoneuroses have, from the beginning of psychoanalysis, been claimed as the special province of psychotherapy. Only more recently has it been found possible to extend psychoanalytical treatment with advantage to some psychotic conditions, often along with the use of medical treatments. For the psychoses, whether organic or psychogenic, such physical remedies as prefrontal leucotomy, sub-insulin coma, electro-convulsive treatment, and drugs, sedative, tranquillizing and anti-depressive are in use, according to the nature of the case. Where the patient is accessible to a psychotherapeutic (or personal relationship) treatment, this is usually carried on (when obtainable) along with the recourse to physical remedies. I had one male patient whose suicidal depression was at first too intense to permit of psychoanalysis, and he was helped over the dangerous phase by sub-insulin coma treatment in hospital. As soon as he was able, he resumed analysis, and his depression, now reduced in intensity though still very definitely there, was successfully cleared up by analytical therapy; and he was able to take up his life again in full. In this case, however, there was no question of his depression being endogenous. It was a definite reaction to a serious and frightening situation in which he suddenly found himself.

In such cases, we have to ask: What is the contribution made respectively by the two different types of treatment? This question raises all the crucial issues about treatment. Usually, when the illness is of psychotic severity (even though psychological in origin) the emotional reactions and associated physical symptoms are too severe to make co-operation in psychotherapy easy or even possible. The symptoms need to be kept under some degree of control, and the emotional tension moderated, so that the patient may be capable of telling the psychotherapist whatever he can about what is happening to him.

The use of physical treatments is not, however, confined to psychotic states. Electro-convulsive therapy (E.C.T.), and even sub-insulin coma given for a severe depression, are best followed up after an interval by steady psychoanalytical therapy. In severe anxiety-states, exhaustion states, and insomnia, the use of tranquillizing, anti-depressive, and sedative drugs is frequently, and sometimes necessarily, combined with psychotherapy in the treatment of the psychoneuroses. These neuroses used to be called 'functional nervous disorders' to indicate that there was no physical disease of whatever parts of the body were involved in the production of symptoms. It was simply that the way the body functioned was disturbed by emotional tension. Parallel to these functional nervous disorders with physical symptoms was another group of 'behavioural disorders', sometimes called 'character neuroses'. Here it was the mental personality rather than the body that was malfunctioning. A hard and fast distinction cannot, however, be sustained between physical and mental 'functional' disorders. 'Obsessional neurosis' is a character disorder, or a mental malfunctioning, for the patient suffers an irresistible compulsion to keep on performing certain acts (such as hand-washing for anything from half an hour to two hours), or is quite unable to suppress the continuous repetitive thinking of certain ideas so that he cannot give his attention to anything else. On the other hand, hysteria is par excellence the physical functional nervous disorder, for the psychic tensions are constantly driven into the body and physical symptoms mask the real emotional conflicts. Nevertheless, the real problem in hysteria is not physical, and after the physical symptoms have been undermined by analysis, we are left with the patient's real personality problems. Furthermore, the obsessional neurosis does not maintain exclusively psychological forms, for the mental obsessions are constantly found to be accompanied by bodily tensions, the 'somatic resonances' of severe anxiety.

Of recent years a third expanding group of illnesses has been isolated under the name of psychosomatic diseases. Here, the physical and psychological elements in the disease are differently related. Long continued tensions in the mental personality have produced, not merely malfunctioning of otherwise healthy organs, but actual damage to bodily tissue. The best known of such diseases include various skin troubles (eczemas, psoriasis), abdominal troubles (such as gastric and duodenal ulcers and colitis), asthma, coronary thrombosis, sinusitis. Research into the group of psychosomatic diseases continues. Here there is both physical and psychological damage existing together, and both must be treated at the same time. The physical condition cannot be allowed to deteriorate further, while the slow process of psychotherapy seeks to remove the causes of the trouble in the personality. Nor can the physical trouble be treated and its roots in emotional tension ignored, or it will only break out again.

We have then four groups of illnesses through which the physical element is of decreasing importance:

(1) *The purely organic illnesses* where mental disturbance is merely secondary, such as general paralysis of the insane (G.P.I.), due to a brain infection. This group no doubt includes some psychotic conditions. In this group the physical disease is really the whole illness.

(2) *Psychosomatic diseases* where there is both physical and psychological illness, and though the first depends on and arises because of the second, it must be treated separately and in its own right.

(3) *Functional nervous disorders, the psychoneuroses,* where physical symptoms do not represent diseased bodily tissues but only the malfunctioning of otherwise healthy organs. Here the physical symptoms may or may not need to be treated, according to their severity, but if they are, the treatment will be purely a matter of *the control or suppression of symptoms,* and will not as such cure the psychological trouble. Its aim is rather to make life more endurable where tensions and symptoms are too severe, and to facilitate psychotherapeutic treatment.

(4) *Functional personality disorders,* such as sexual deviations, delinquent and criminal behaviour, cold and unfeeling personality, temper outbursts. Here there may be no physical symptoms at all.

Different Levels of Treatment

We are now in a position to see what is really accomplished by the different levels of treatment, which we shall distinguish as physical, social and psychological. There is everywhere, as one would expect, a constant interweaving of physical and mental symptoms in the patterns of mental illness. This is a problem easily, though spuriously, resolved by the old-fashioned materialist, who simply assumes that the body causes everything. This line of approach simply does not work in clinical practice. The problem is more usually thought of as the interaction of body and mind, and in a rough and ready way this is a true enough description. We are not thereby committed to philosophical dualism, the belief that matter and mind are two entirely separate and distinct entities. We cannot know the ultimate truth in this matter. The limitations of the human intellect do not permit such knowledge. For practical purposes, however, we have to make a distinction between two different aspects of what in some ultimate sense must be one whole.

Thus, if a man becomes mentally confused because he has been hit on the head by a brick, the cause is indisputably 'purely physical'. If he becomes mentally confused because of the sudden emotional shock of the news that his wife has been knocked down and killed, the cause is indisputably 'purely psychological'; and this is still true when we take into account that the total experience involves glandular secretions that disturb the body, for these are stimulated by the extreme anxiety of the shock. If a man becomes insane because of spirochaete infection of the brain, the causation again is purely physical. If a man breaks down into a frantic and tortured state of mind because all through his childhood he has been treated with such exceptional cruelty that he cannot now master any longer the tempestuous emotions that rend him from within, the cause must be considered definitely psychological.

We can set aside the purely physical cases as not belonging to the category of 'mental illness' in our present sense. They are problems for physical medicine. For the rest we shall find an intermixing of mental and physical symptoms in such a way that, for the purposes of treatment, we may approach the mental personality either or both through the body by physical means, and direct by psychological means as in psychotherapy. In the *psychosomatic diseases* serious damage has been done to bodily tissues, and physical medicine is indispensable immediately for dealing with the somatic aspect of the illness; while a prolonged psychological approach is being made to the tensions within the personality which are the primary long-term cause of injury to the body. This can easily involve going deeply into the whole life-history of the patient.

In the *psychoneurotic or functional nervous disorders* ('nerves') the situation is different. If the physical symptoms are treated by physical methods, it is not because there is a dangerous and deteriorating condition of bodily tissues. The body itself is healthy and sound, but its functioning is disturbed by emotional stress. Anxiety may set up palpitation of the heart, sweating, pallor, trembling, all of which symptoms will disappear as soon as the anxiety dies down. One patient developed eczema of the hands when her parents decided to go abroad and leave her in lodgings, and it cleared up as soon as they cancelled their decision. Another patient suffering from 'migraine' developed an attack in session while talking of her parents' quarrels in her childhood. This 'migraine' disappeared entirely when she had at last talked out these memories so thoroughly as to leave little emotion attached to them. During the course of analysis, transient physical symptoms often come and go, such as constipation or diarrhoea, sickness, retention of urine or frequency of micturition, indigestion, various muscular aches and pains often in the back of the neck or small of the back, and so on, varying with the development and resolution of particular emotional problems. Sometimes these symptoms become so severe, and, if the mental conflict cannot be quickly resolved, so prolonged, that it is necessary to fall back on some medical means of controlling or moderating the symptom, in the interests of the patient's need to carry on his normal life. Yet it is not necessarily a good thing to suppress the symptom altogether, by means usually of drugs, for it is itself an incentive to understand and resolve the conflict that produces it. If the symptom is suppressed, the conflict may be merely repressed, and an illusory sense of being 'much better' is then an escape from the real issues. This is equally true when E.C.T. or drugs are used to abate purely emotional symptoms such as intense anxiety, excitement or apathy.

Nevertheless, it is certainly true that there are cases, and occasions, where anxiety is so severe and the struggle to keep going is so exhausting, that psychotherapy must call in the aid of the appropriate drug to enable the patient to cope with both real life responsibilities and treatment at the same time. *In the psychosomatic diseases the physical and psychological treatments may be regarded as equal partners. In the neuroses, the physical treatments are auxiliary to the psychological, which is the only real treatment of the illness.* There are many psychiatrists, perhaps a majority, who still do not take this view, and who want to regard the whole problem as basically one of physical medicine, but I do not know anyone trained and experienced in psychotherapy who agrees with that. It is those who have little or no genuine experience of psychotherapy who are so ready to discard it altogether. We shall go more fully into this problem later.

In the *behavioural disorders or character neuroses*, there may at the outset be no physical symptoms at all. Many a bad tempered or aggressive person works out all his or her tensions on other people and takes the strain off his own body. Such people remain physically fit while the other members of the family become ill with the strain of coping with them. The extremely cold, detached person may keep emotion at a low ebb all the time by his very 'out-of-touchness' and refusal to allow life to make any impact on him. He may go on smoothly and in good health for years, though not seldom sooner or later the signs eventually appear of hidden tensions taking their toll of the body. But if a patient with a personality problem and no physical symptoms comes for psychoanalytic treatment, it usually happens that as his secret inner conflicts are released by analysis, his struggles begin to manifest themselves in more recognizable and symptomatic form. The case then begins to approximate more to the psychoneuroses, just as a successful treatment of a psychoneurosis with physical symptoms has the opposite effect, of turning it steadily into a character problem as the physical symptoms clear up. We must, then, seek to define the nature and roles of physical and psychological methods of treatment respectively.

A third line of approach must here be brought into the picture, *the social approach*, where an attempt is made to alleviate the pressures in real life that trigger off the patient's long-standing liability to severe anxiety, by means of improvements in his real life situation. I shall briefly indicate my conclusions at once before I elaborate the discussion. Taking the modern psychiatric drugs as representative of the physical treatments, I would say that drugs suppress the symptoms but do not touch the real illness, since they have no power to produce any maturing of the personality. Social measures, to lessen the pressure of the environment on the patient and give him a better chance of remaining well, must always be taken where possible and will alleviate the illness without curing it. Psychological treatment, particularly psychoanalysis, at least seeks to deal with the illness itself, the disturbed and distorted set-up within the patient's personality, and to produce a radical cure by aiming to promote the genuine development of the patient as a person towards greater stability. We have then three levels of treatment, *Alleviation* by social measures, *Suppression* by medical measures, and *Attempted Radical Cure* by psychological measures.

2. *The Alleviation of Mental Illness by Social Measures*

I take this first because it is non-controversial in principle. I do not think that anyone will disagree that if a patient's human and material environment remains too hostile and unhelpful, none of the other methods will have any great chance of success. My help was once sought by a woman whose life was being made an utter misery by a brutal and uncomprehending husband. She was not prepared to leave him and it was clear that her 'illness' was the only protection she had. It at least kept a doctor in attendance and was some kind of check on the husband. I did not attempt to treat her. I merely said that I could not see how she could be other than ill under the strain of her marriage, which she freely recognized and admitted. It would be foolish to expect psychotherapy to clear up the neurotic problems of a young husband or wife, if the couple were living with unsympathetic in-laws. While there is a real problem of loneliness in old age, there is also a problem of neurosis breaking out in middle age when a difficult aged parent comes to live in the home.

There are many ways in which the environment can press unreasonably hard on the individual. No one can expect to go through life without having difficulties to face, but there is a point at which frustration and hardship cease to be an invigorating spur to effort, and begin to undermine and break down a person's resistance to stress. This is especially true when the individual has already been overstrained in childhood. He may then break down under difficulties and burdens which would not have that effect on other more fortunate people. Psychiatry has evolved the Psychiatric Social Worker (the P.S.W.) whose function it is to find out if practical domestic, economic or social measures need to be taken where possible, to give the patient a more helpful world to live in, and to give the psychiatric or psychotherapeutic treatments a better chance of success. Problems of work, housing, in-law responsibilities and many other such questions come under this head.

It is not always the case that people break down in an unhappy environment where they would not do so in a normally happy supporting one. Sometimes depressed persons become more depressed if their environment is too good, and feel better if they have things they can get openly and frankly angry about, or abuses and wrongs they can attack. Those whose depression contains more of fear and apathy than of guilt, however, are more likely to break down in bad situations where they would feel more supported in good ones. These are problems for the psychotherapist rather than the social worker.

Nevertheless, psychotherapy cannot make headway against an impossibly stressful environment. Broadly speaking, a patient with a thoroughly understanding marriage partner has a much better chance of recovery under psychotherapy than a person married to a cruel, inconsiderate or selfish partner. The P.S.W., where available, can often help greatly by talking over the whole problem of the patient's illness with the husband or wife, where it would be unwise or impossible for the therapist to see both parties. In the psychotherapy of children, it is a regular thing for a P.S.W.

to see the parents. Dr. Balint, in his work in training seminars with G.P.s, finds that his groups have come to think in terms not so much of the ill patient as of the ill family, and in terms of which is the member of the family who is most ill and most affecting the others: this may not be the person who comes for treatment. Thus the environment cannot be left out of account. This was once brought home to me from a different point of view. I had a young patient who had not been blessed with the average amenities of domestic life. For a time he entered a very good mental hospital while he carried on his analytical treatment with me, and said: 'I've never lived in such a lovely place'. After his sojourn there he made good progress, got away from home and established himself.

3. *The Suppression of Mental Illness by Medical Measures*

In Part 1 we considered the traditional 'moral diagnosis' of personality disorders, and it is relevant here to say that the age-old methods of moral exhortation and educational discipline applied to disturbed persons, are attempts to suppress an illness by enforcing control of its manifestations. The real trouble is not cured but covered over. Such methods aimed as much at the protection and convenience of other people as at the 'cure' or 'reformation' of the individual whose reactions to life were disturbing those around him. At a rough and ready common sense level, no doubt, attempts to deal with such problems by these means will always be made, until in each separate case it comes to be realized that the person concerned is in need of specialized help.

Indeed, patients have always tried to deal with themselves along these lines before they seek other help. They will say how upset they are about their worrying and bad temper, how bad they feel they must be for other members of the family, and how hard they struggle to control themselves, only to find that their internal tensions repeatedly get the better of them. It is, of course, clear that if they were not trying to control their outbursts, these would become much more frequent until the neurosis would replace the realistic self of everyday living. If we could but know their whole story, no doubt the success they achieve is greater than they are given credit for. We certainly must not despise this attempt to resist and suppress personality disorders, but accept the failures with sympathetic understanding.

However, because moral self-control becomes less effective the more ill the patient is, the responsibility for suppressing the illness is to a considerable extent taken over today by medical treatments. We must now, therefore, consider the nature and functions of modern psychiatry. If there was little that was controversial about social alleviation, there is controversy in plenty about psychiatry and psychotherapy.

Developments in Modern Psychiatry

For our present purposes 'modern psychiatry' can be taken to mean the treatment provided by the mental hospital of the present day. Like other hospitals and all human institutions, some are better than others in facilities and progressive outlook. Some, unfortunately, make little attempt to understand the personality of the patient, but at its best, the mental hospital of today is a more enlightened institution than in the days of mere custodial care. I recently heard a male nurse who had spent all his working life at the same hospital say: 'When I first came here it was just care, rest or restraint. Nowadays we give real treatment.' It is important, however, to understand what can and cannot be done in the mental hospital, for false expectations lead to unnecessary disillusionment. Mental hospital treatment is roughly a combination of physical methods of cutting short acute attacks, reducing symptoms, and suppressing the deep emotional causes of the illness, while at the same time building up the social and working self of the conscious level by rehabilitation measures, care for physical health, brief psychotherapy, art therapy, occupational therapy and outdoor activities. It is at one and the same time treatment and a 'holiday with a purpose', a relief from the pressures of life with help for the patient to recover stability. The mental hospital plays a vital part in combating mental ill-health, and we must look to the future for their great further improvement, and for a reduction of popular prejudices and fears in making voluntary use of them. At the same time, not all such hospitals are on the level of the best ones, and the intelligent patient has a right to know what is the type and outlook of the institution to which he is entrusting his mental health.

The approach of the mental hospital is different from, but ought not to be thought of as conflicting with, the psychoanalytic and general psychotherapeutic approach. Briefly, we might summarize the difference as between fairly quick restabilization and slow redevelopment of the personality. Long-term psychotherapy aims to provide a supportive relationship in which, as insight grows, and as the patient feels secure in being understood and respected as a person, a radical regrowth of the personality can take place with the elimination of the old fears and hates. In the mental hospital there is no time for more than slight short-term psychotherapy in some cases, and that depends very much on the individual psychiatrist's outlook and interest. The psychotherapist spends a very great deal of time with a few patients, and radical psychotherapy is too long a process to be possible in hospital. Moreover, it is most desirable that a patient having radical psychotherapy should, if at all possible, be at the same time living in the world and coming up against the problems of everyday living. It is his reactions to these that provide many of the best opportunities for psychotherapeutic work. In hospital a small psychiatric staff have to deal with a very large number of patients and cannot attempt the impossible.

But it is also quite possible to combine, when necessary, the two methods of the hospital and the long-term psychotherapeutic approach. I have had a number of patients who, in times of severe emotional crisis, entered hospital. The too badly disturbed person cannot immediately co-operate in psychoanalytical investigation or in anything else. He needs, for his own protection, to have his acute tensions relieved as quickly as possible, by physical methods of treatment. Then, with the period of recuperation which a hospital can provide, he is restored to a condition where he can carry on with his daily life and either start or resume the long-term treatment which aims to reach and relieve the deep down causes of the trouble, and support his slow and spontaneous re-growth into a more basically stable personality.

It is unhappily true that in this, as in other fields, some workers lose perspective and acquire such an emotional over-attachment to their own particular line, coupled with not much real knowledge of the other types of treatment, that they tend to decry methods different from their own. The most experienced people do not fall into this trap, but one can find psychiatrists who are hostile to radical psychotherapy as taking far too long, and leading to too great dependence of the patient on the therapist (objections we shall presently consider), and psychotherapists who too hastily dismiss psychiatric treatments as superficial. The fact is that we cannot do without either approach. Some types of personality can make much more effective use of radical psychotherapy than others, and in the end the issue will be decided (apart from acute crises) by what the patient wants and is really aiming at. I have had patients who gladly welcomed both kinds of treatment according to their changing needs, and others who have been saved from hospitalization by long-term psychoanalytic treatment. Shorter treatments can be made available for far more people, while long-term treatments in the nature of the case are far more dependent on the coincidence of a variety of factors, the right type of patient, the right type of therapist, sufficiently stable circumstances to permit the treatment to continue, and, by no means the least factor, reasonably understanding relatives. Not only must the patient be able to keep on coming, but also the psychotherapist must not move away and 'take a job' elsewhere. We shall consider presently the difficulties involved in radical psychotherapy. It is, however, true that many intelligent patients who have a real appreciation of the nature of personality and its problems are far from being content with the results of short-term treatments which are not by any means always lasting, and are determined if they can find it to get more adequate help.

The issue of 'dependence on the therapist' is the one point at which there can arise a genuine divergence of viewpoint based, I am sure ultimately, on a misunderstanding of what is involved. It is often argued, quite unrealistically, that psychoanalysis makes the patient dependent on the analyst. Put in that form, the criticism bears no relationship to the realities of the problem. Psychoanalysis does not create the 'dependence'. It has discovered it to be the essence of the illness, as the two previous chapters aimed to show, and it is usually overlooked that marked signs of such dependence have already appeared in other directions long before the patient came to the analyst. The analyst is the first person who has been in a position to accept the dependence and use it in a constructive way to provide opportunity to grow greater inner strength. This question will be more fully dealt with later. At this stage we need only say that many people who really need long-term treatment, if only they could get it, have to make do with the short-term rehabilitation which psychiatry can supply. The result, no doubt, is that patients are got over a crisis for the time being, and in a year or two may have to go through it all again, perhaps having repeated hospitalizations, recoveries, and disappointing repetitions of breakdown. This cannot be said to be anybody's fault. Not everyone is able to profit by deep psychoanalysis, but even then I cannot think it is within reach of attainment to provide it even for all those who could. Our resources for treating mental illness are simply grossly inadequate to the widespread need, and the best that is at present possible is constantly being improved on. If the money devoted by Russia and America to landing rockets on the moon were to be devoted to mental health, our real Number One Priority, no doubt far better facilities for treatment, even on the basis of our existing knowledge, would be possible for all nations. Furthermore, our understanding of the causes of mental illness are only just beginning to reach down to the deepest depths of the personality. A public opinion intelligently informed and alive to the situation would be the best stimulus for making possible far better work for mental health.

That the present situation does lead to tragic disillusionment is proved by the following letter, only one of many such brought to me over the last ten years by the publication of *You and Your Nerves*.

'I am seeking help and advice. . . . I am a married woman with one child. I have suffered from an anxiety neurosis for the past 15 years and have had treatment for the past six years following a breakdown which ended in depression. I was relieved of this depression by 12 E.C.T., and was discharged from hospital after a four months stay, still suffering from anxiety. Since then I have seen one psychiatrist after another in the hope of finding a cure, and was told I needed deep psychoanalysis after being treated with 8 more E.C.T., drugs, pentothal, and gas. . . .That is a somewhat sketchy history of my case, but I wish to emphasize my desire to get better and to be as good a wife and mother as possible. I have found over the past years very little understanding even among doctors, and when I have told them that I have no further use for shock treatment or drugs they seem at a loss. The psychiatrist who told me I needed deep psychoanalysis helped me enormously, but I seek a permanent cure if that is at all possible. I have been told, and I know it to be true, that it is necessary for me to change. I am eager for this but I must find someone who can help me. Sometimes in my blacker moments I feel absolutely forsaken by God and man, and it is this helplessness that has driven me to write to you.'

This letter reveals the real poignancy and tragedy of mental illness and is far too important a human document to be ignored. We must be careful not to draw the wrong conclusion from it. It does not mean that mental hospital treatment is useless. It would be possible to find other people whose lives had been lifted on to a definitely more secure level by their sojourn in hospital. But it did not work for this patient, and there are many like her. The psychiatrist who helped her most saw that she needed long-term psychotherapy. Unfortunately *no one specifically trained for long-term psychotherapy* was available, which emphasizes the inadequacy of our resources. The above correspondent showed great determination not to be put off with anything less than the deep psychotherapy she needed, and wrote later to tell me that she had found someone near enough to her area who really could help her, and she had taken a job to get treatment. She said :

'My life is beginning to take on a new meaning, very slowly I must admit, and sometimes very painfully, but I am determined to carry on because I believe that it is worth anything to be a healthy, happy, contented wife and mother and to have peace of mind which I could never have had by any other means.'

Remembering that the hospital did relieve her of the bad depression which started her six years of breakdown, and that then she had to be discharged still suffering from anxiety, it is clear that that was the ideal time for deep psychotherapy to be started, if not earlier. It highlights the great need for 'combined operations' for many patients, as between the hospital and the psychotherapist, if only the resources existed.

The following case throws an important light on the problem of 'dependence'. I once had a severely obsessional patient referred to me, for whom the brain operation known as prefrontal leucotomy had been suggested. However, it was decided to try psychoanalysis first and a long analytical treatment made the operation unnecessary. If someone should be critical of the length of the analysis, it would be entirely relevant to say: However long it took, dependence on the help of an understanding human being in a healing relationship is better than a brain operation. I shall not discuss this extreme measure of prefrontal leucotomy. It is only likely to be recommended as a last desperate remedy when all other measures have failed, and it is a matter for expert psychiatric opinion. But even then it needs to be borne in mind that in some cases it may be resorted to, not because all other measures are ineffective, but because the real alternative of long-term analytical therapy is unobtainable. This does, however, serve to bring out the fact that there is not really any 'issue' between psychiatry and psychoanalysis, unless narrow-mindedness creates one. It is a question of choice between physical and rehabilitating modes of suppressing the illness quickly, and psychological, i.e. personal methods of promoting a regrowth of personality. We cannot do without either, and with our present knowledge neither work with infallible certainty. Psychotherapy has its difficulties and limitations as well as psychiatry, as we shall presently discuss. Under these circumstances it is important that there should be clear and widespread understanding of what can reasonably be expected from both types of treatment, so that false hopes and disillusionments are avoided. Mental Health Year, and Radio and TV propaganda have, I have observed, created in some people a dangerous optimism supported by superficial knowledge, that modern science enables miracles to be performed in the sphere of mental illness. In sober fact, that is as far from the truth as it could well be.

Psychiatric Drugs

We shall understand the action of psychiatric drugs, and the role of physical treatments in general best, if we first remind ourselves of what it is that has to be treated. In Parts 1 and 2 we saw how the personality as a whole loses its unity and coherence under the stress of too early difficulties in personal relationships which are beyond the child's capacity to cope with. So many conflicting feelings are roused in him that as he grows he becomes mentally 'split' into several one-sided partial selves, instead of being one whole united strong self. Different people are not by any means equally conscious and aware of these internal divisions. Mental illness is civil war in the mind, and the ultimate conflict is between an emotionally injured child-self in the grip of fear, feeling powerless and unable to cope, and the rest of the personality which struggles to counteract all that and go on coping with existence in the outer world. Furthermore the child in the grip of fear remains the centre of still warring emotions, gathered mainly into the two opposite reactions of retreat and fighting back. At different times, the child in distress inside the struggling adult presents a variety of different faces to life; a hungry, love-starved, needy, greedy child who breaks through in symptoms such as compulsive eating or stealing or sexual excitements or an intense craving for affection, appreciation or attention; an angry, frustrated, resentful child, fighting to compel a response to his needs, and appearing to other people to be selfish and inconsiderate; a guilt-burdened child whose problems with himself and other folk have undermined his self-respect and drive him into punishing himself mentally, and sometimes physically as in 'accident proneness' or the development of painful physical symptoms; and a timid, fear-ridden child who reacts with acute apprehension to everything, and is at bottom in retreat from life, withdrawing into himself, and losing all natural and healthy rapport with the world around him. In the face of all this, the conscious self of everyday living struggles to master the accumulating internal tensions and control their outbreak into disturbed behaviour. The more successful this control, the more likelihood there is of the tensions being dammed up in the body to cause physical disturbances. We are reminded of the old saying: 'A city divided against itself cannot stand'. An overall sense of weakness and inadequacy dominates the entire personality.

Faced with this situation, each patient must in the long run decide whether he wants merely to be rid of his symptoms at whatever cost to his personality, or whether he wants ultimately, like the letter-writer quoted, to achieve a fuller and freer capacity to live. In practice this issue is never quite such a simple choice as it may here appear to be. We shall consider first the medical methods of trying to cut off and suppress the manifestations of a highly disturbed and deep-seated emotional life. This way of putting it may be misleading for it suggests that emotions are things-in-themselves which cause us trouble, a false simplification.

We must instead think of a 'total person' feeling in certain ways because of the situation, external and internal, that he feels to be in. In insomnia, for example, it is particularly important to approach the problem in this way, for this troublesome symptom develops usually at times when the person concerned is most in need of rest and he appears to be unable to let himself have it. The individual undermined in childhood and feeling inadequate to meet the demands of adult living, feels he must struggle and strive all the harder, summon up all his energy, put forth unremitting effort or he will never be able to keep going. Thus he gets into the state of mind of being afraid to relax and is unable to commit himself to the passive inactivity of sleep. It is as if deep down he were afraid that if once he stops he will not be able to start again. Thus the very effort to keep going becomes exhausting and contributes to breakdown. While the hidden fears and motives that sustain this self-defeating over-activity by night as well as day are being investigated, it is often essential to allow some rest to the whole system by means of some sleeping drug.

It is more constructive, in so far as it is possible, to depend on a human being, a psychotherapist, than on a drug, if a radical change of personality is being sought. It is often possible for a patient who has had to accept the support of drugs prior to securing psychoanalytic treatment, to dispense with them once he has begun to find security in the analytic relationship. But in two instances the use of drugs is essential, namely, when psychotherapy cannot be obtained, and when, even though the patient is having psychotherapeutic treatment, his anxiety and tension are as yet too severe to enable him to stand analytic treatment and at the same time cope with everyday living without the help drugs can provide.

At this point it seems necessary to comment on the extraordinary multiplication of psychiatric drugs through the researches of industrial chemists, which is something of a phenomenon in our time. I do not find doctors feeling very happy about it. These drugs divide broadly into the 'anti-depressives' or stimulants, and the 'tranquillizers' or sedatives. Anti-depressives or stimulants are 'energizers', aiming to relieve states of apathy, loss of interest, and exhaustion. They seek to combat the *passive* neurosis which we have traced to an ultimate deep-seated fear and longing to take flight from life, the undermining pull of the fear-ridden child within. The tranquillizers are much more talked of and have become something of a byword. The fact that the name has caught on so markedly is sure proof of the extent to which 'tension' is recognized as a destructive factor in modern life. The tranquillizers aim to produce relaxation of tension, to damp down anxiety, and put a brake on the chronic over-driving of the self in the *active* neuroses. Their name is legion and it is easy to find doctors who have never prescribed many of them, and who regard those they have tried with distinct reservations.

Often an anti-depressive and a tranquillizer are prescribed together to give energy while controlling tension. It is naturally necessary for the patient to observe as accurately as he can the effect the prescribed drug or drugs are having on him, as the physician will need to vary either the drug or the dosage till the desired effect is obtained. I have found a number of patients complain that some tranquillizer was damping them down too much, reducing not only anxiety but all their other feelings as well and making them feel detached, out of touch and impersonal. The dose then needs to be reduced. However, one patient who found that a particular drug was having this effect on her was nevertheless helped over a particularly anxious period in her life by it, and doubtless feeling somewhat too detached was better, under the circumstances, than feeling uncontrolled emotion, to her own and other people's distress. That, of course, is not a 'cure' of anything, but it is a valuable mental splint or crutch at a time of crisis. Too much persisting tension over long periods, when there is no opportunity of relieving it by undermining its deep-seated mental causes, is often 'controlled' or at least abated somewhat by the phenobarbitone which everyone nowadays has heard of. Life would be harder to bear for many people if they could not relieve headaches by aspirin, disprin or codeine. The prescription of a balanced combination of anti-depressive and tranquillizing drugs is, however, intended to build up its effectiveness slowly over a period and then to maintain a state of stability which can make life possible for the seriously mentally ill person.

We are bound nevertheless to take seriously the fact that many patients find the use of drugs very disappointing. One patient of mine, who, in a critical period, found it so difficult to control her emotions that she was afraid of losing her job, found the prescription of an anti-depressive and a tranquillizer extremely useful for enabling her to cope reasonably calmly with her work. After three months she felt she had got over the crisis period, and then said, 'I'm going to have to stop taking these drugs. They are making me an artificial person. I feel more real and am more "me" when I'm anxious; and now they're stopping me making progress in the analysis.' Over the next month she reduced them and was then able to carry on without them and proceed with the psycho-therapeutic analysis. I have several times found a patient caught in the dilemma of the drug suppressing either too much or too little emotion, or else finding that dependence on the drug has itself become a problem calling for psychological treatment.

Professor G. M. Carstairs, in his Reith Lectures for 1963, stated his opinion that 'the most neglected field in medical science today is the psychological study of mental illness', and he then went on to say:

'All too often doctors seem to think only in terms of brain disease, as though a person's mind could be treated as simply as his liver. Perhaps nowhere in contemporary society can we see such clear evidence of the persistence of magical thinking as in the doctor's willingness to be persuaded (perhaps half-persuaded) that the drug houses have newly discovered the elixir of life. In recent years extravagant hopes have been centred on the psychotropic drugs, drugs which will relieve agitation and depression, and others which calm the turmoil of the acutely deranged. These drugs are often effective, if only for a time; but they have been used so intemperately that we still know remarkably little about their scope and limitations and their possible dangers; and yet they are being prescribed today in their millions. I do not want to deny the help that these drugs have brought to many seriously ill patients, but only to point out that when they are taken to relieve the emotional distress caused by problems of living they are merely an anodyne, and offer no lasting solution. Even physical dis-comfort becomes bearable when it is found to have meaning and a limit. On the other hand, neurotic distress is greatest when it appears to be incomprehensible. To allay the symptom while failing to explore, and if possible eradicate, the cause has always been bad medicine. Why then have we tolerated it so long where neurotic illness is concerned?'

Some of the answers to that question will, I hope, begin to emerge in the next three chapters.

At this point we must ask, where do we, in our general outlook, pass from the valuable medically prescribed use of tension-relievers and stimulants to help the suffering over critical stages of their illness, to a view of life based on the constant support of drugs? The combination of biochemical research and the chronic insecurity of modern civilization (an insidious mental insecurity for most people rather than a blatant economic and material one) seems to be producing a pattern of needing sedatives at night, stimulants in the morning and tranquillizers during the day, and also an atmosphere and mental outlook which makes it difficult for psychotherapy to get at the real emotional situation in the background. Is it that the increasing pace and pressure of living, under the unremitting speeding up of everything by scientific invention, is steadily forcing us into a 'drug-addict philosophy of life'. Science helps us to create the tensions which it then helps us to damp down again, a vicious circle which is not at all likely to lead to universal mental health.

As long ago as 1908 Freud found neurologists who 'loudly proclaimed the connection between the "increasing nervousness" of the present day and modern civilized life'.* He quoted from a neurologist, Dr. W. Erb, who wrote: 'Life in large cities is constantly becoming more elaborate and more restless. The exhausted nerves seek recuperation in increased stimulation . . . only thereby to become more exhausted than before.'† He cited Von Krafft-Ebing as writing, of the rapid changes that occur in modern civilization, that the 'nervous system . . . is then called upon to meet the increased social and domestic demands by a greater expenditure of energy, unredressed by any satisfactory forms of recuperation'.‡ Freud himself regarded this opinion as 'not erroneous' but he was clear that physical exhaustion of physical nerves was not a complete or satisfactory explanation of nervous illness. He realized that there must be a psychological, emotional, personality-factor at work, and he concluded that what had been overlooked by the neurologists was the essential factor of 'sexual inhibition'.‡ Since Freud first developed his views, however, there has come about a very great degree of relaxation of sexual inhibitions, and yet this has had no effect whatever in diminishing neurosis. In fact, it is clear that the most sexually uninhibited people are very highly disturbed persons, that indiscriminate sexual activity is a tension-relieving outlet, and that sexual problems are symptoms not causes of neurosis. Yet Freud was right

* *Collected Papers*, Vol. 2, p. 78.
† Op. cit. p. 79.
‡ Ibid. p. 80.

to seek to trace neurosis to some roots in the mental personality and not regard it as simply due to physical nervous exhaustion.

We have here traced the cause of neurosis rather to fear, and especially to the fears of earliest origin. These result in a powerful and persisting undercurrent of feelings of inferiority and inadequacy and weakness in the face of the tasks of adult life. This enables us to understand even more clearly how it is that the pressures of life in the present day bring about the actual outbreak of a nervous illness. The patient does not feel equal to life anyway, and the more exhausting, intense and pressing life becomes, the more deep-level anxiety accumulates. I have had many patients who exhibited entirely understandable reactions, not only of anxiety in a more general sense but sheer fear, at the intense pressure put upon them by the ruthless competitiveness of modern industrial and commercial life, and often simply at the sheer amount of work they had to get through, which could not in every case be explained away as due to a compulsion to overwork and take too much on. All this is backed by political and international rivalries, which make a direct emotional impact on the individual far more today than used to be the case. We can hardly afford nowadays to allow a child to have a cultural education. We must train up scientists to keep us ahead of other nations in the race for power and possession, or even for sheer survival. All this has never been so intense in the whole history of the world as it is today. There was more truth in the views of the neurologists of 1908, if only they had been alive to the psychological factor in exhaustion, than Freud allowed for; but if it was true over fifty years ago, how far more true is it now. Many patients today openly voice their fears of an atom war.

Both nations and individuals live in fear and in a longing for security, and if the deep hidden roots of this in the unconscious are a legacy of infancy and childhood, modern so-called 'civilization' does its best to play on and activate that internal danger. If all our mental health services can offer in the long run is drugs to combat the tension and produce an artificial tranquillization of the body which cannot be really shared by the mental self, then we shall have to regard this situation as one more symptom of the chronic self-destructive dilemma of the 'civilization' of our time. The difficulty about drugs is that as the tension increases, so the need for drugs increases. As a doctor said to me recently: 'To stop your emotions coming through you've got to take enough of the drug to put yourself out. If you don't, your feelings will get through anyway.' That is why, valuable as drugs can be at critical periods, wisely prescribed by the understanding physician, we cannot possibly regard drugs as 'the magic cure'. They are a 'very present help in time of trouble' but people also need personal help for their personality as such.

Only a brief word need be added about Electro-Convulsive Therapy (E.C.T.) since it does not raise any different question in principle from those we have already considered in the case of drugs. It is a purely empirical symptom-relieving procedure, and when it is the only treatment given, the first course of 'shocks' may have to be repeated several times. Some patients arrive at the point where it is deemed inadvisable to have more. Its effects in disturbing memory are transient and pass off after a month or so. I have been told of one case in which E.C.T. suppressed not only the patient's anxiety but also her artistic interests and activity, thus considerably changing her personality for some two years. These, however, eventually returned as the patient proceeded with psychoanalysis. A number of my own patients had E.C.T. at a critical phase and they all without exception benefited, and were able to resume analysis afterwards with greater ability to co-operate. Where drugs or E.C.T. are used, it should be combined with psychotherapy.

Hypnosis

An equally brief word may be said about this here, since, although it is not a physical treatment, it is most popularly known in the form of 'hypnotic suggestion' as a means of suppressing symptoms. In this case, as with drugs, the effect wears off and no permanent cure results. The other use of hypnosis, namely as a means of bringing repressed memories back to consciousness, is being more reliably taken over by drugs such as pentothal, and the later L.S.D. (lysergic acid diethylamide). Undoubtedly such drugs can 'disinhibit' the personality and allow the deeper and normally repressed mental levels to break through into consciousness. The best known mild disinhibitor is alcohol. The psychiatric disinhibitors can facilitate the return to consciousness of astonishingly early experiences. They are being much used today by psychiatrists who seek to short-cut psycohanalysis while hoping to achieve the same results. I myself view this process with marked suspicion. It forces back to consciousness material which the conscious self is not prepared to receive and accept, with the result that it is either repressed again and forgotten as the drug wears off, or the personality is unwisely subjected to stresses it is not ready to cope with. I have not come across any evidence that these 'tin opener' methods of either hypnosis or drugs have produced in a short time any results comparable to those produced over a longer time by a successful psycho-analytic treatment. They should be used sparingly, and as far as possible with the patient's understanding of what is involved. The slow process of psychoanalysis, which goes at the patient's own pace, is safest.

Supplementary Note

There is a very recent paper in the *British Journal of Psychiatry*, July 1963, by Dr. A. Hordern and Professor Max Hamilton, entitled 'Drugs and "Moral Treatment" '. I summarize their con-clusions, with quotations, under three heads. (1) A century ago the best mental hospitals gave a highly personal, human and social type of treatment with results as good as any held to be produced later by drugs. 'The results obtained by drugs have not bettered the results of those pioneers who introduced "moral treatment" over a century ago.' The term 'moral treatment' is misleading since it may give the impression of 'moral exhortation, discipline, etc.'. In fact it was what today we call personal, or personal-relations, treatment. (2) 'One factor is very potent in affecting the response of patients to drugs—the type of environ-ment, in the sense of the interpersonal care and attention that patients receive.' Drugs are reported to have produced most marked results in the worst, i.e. most impersonal hospital environments. It would seem that then they function as a defence against a bad environment. One investigation by Cooper concluded that the best results were achieved by combining personal and drug treatments. That is my own experience with the most ill patients. (3) 'Drugs tended to exert some inhibitory effects on the improvement obtained by occupational therapy.' That is also my experience in relation to psychotherapy, except at times of acute emotional crisis.

CHAPTER TEN

PSYCHOTHERAPY: A GENERAL SURVEY

1. *Psychotherapy—A Controversial Problem*

WE come finally to the third type of treatment, psychotherapy, which goes beyond attempts at suppression and alleviation of the illness, and makes the bold and difficult attempt to find a radical cure. Psychotherapy is probably the most controversial problem in the whole field of medicine. Naturally, the more far-reaching and comprehensive are the results we aim at, the more we expose ourselves to failures and partial successes. It is often forgotten by critics of psychotherapy that it is an attempt to discover a radical psychological treatment of the causes rather than the symptoms of nervous or personality illness. We have seen, however, that the same liability to failure and partial success dogs the footsteps of the other methods as well, and in any case the search for the radical and fundamental cure must go on. *We may describe psychotherapy as the use of psychological investigation of personality, character-pattern, and life problems in the setting of a reliable and good human relationship with the psychotherapist; so that as insight into the causes and nature of his neurotic anxieties and conflicts grows the patient may be able to use the emotional security of the relationship with the therapist to develop a personality increasingly free from internal causes of fear, and therefore increasingly stable and self-assured.* Ideally, psychotherapy ought to go along with all other kinds of treatment when they are used, and for the most part only lack of time or opportunity, and lack of psychotherapists, prevents that being the case.

Psychotherapy has recently come in for considerable public and critical discussion in the daily press and in magazines. It can be 'written up' in somewhat sensational ways, though this does not create the best atmosphere for the consideration of this exceedingly difficult undertaking. It seems to be assumed that psychotherapy is a clear-cut and definite 'thing', as much so as E.C.T., and that its results ought to be capable of exact assessment and prediction. It is not usually taken into account that psychotherapy is not a rigid and uniform procedure, that it is very far from playing its proper part in the treatment of emotional illness today, that the number of genuinely trained psychotherapists, particularly outside London, is very small, and many who could benefit by this treatment simply cannot find a psychotherapist to go to, that much of what is called psychotherapy is amateurish and hardly worthy of the name, and the whole situation calls for careful survey. It is, for example, not only true that many patients cannot find psychotherapists; many who could become excellent psychotherapists cannot find any adequate training for the work, and this applies as much to medical as to non-medical persons. The sheer length and cost of the training is prohibitive for most candidates. Thus most of the amateur psychotherapy available is offered by medically qualified persons. As one psychiatrist put it to me, 'We are taught the dosage of drugs but not the dosage of doctor'. Many who see the need for psychotherapy and apply themselves to it without the advantage of specific training, clearly attain to considerable experience, but it cannot be good enough in such an important matter to leave psychotherapy to be self-taught : those who have marked natural gifts for such work will find their way, but many who could do good work need the help of systematic training. This is not questioned in any other branch of medicine, or indeed in any profession.

It is not necessary for a psychotherapist to be a medical person; many of the leading Freudian analysts are not medical doctors. What is necessary is that first the psychotherapist, whether medical or not, should be specifically trained for this particular kind of work, and second that it should be carried on in close co-operation with the medical profession. A non-medical psychotherapist should be in touch with the patient's General Practitioner (who ought therefore to be able to satisfy himself that the psychotherapist is a bona fide trained person) and also, according to the severity of the case, with a psychiatrist. It is to be hoped that in course of time trained psychotherapists will be attached to, or in some way associated with, every mental hospital, so that psychotherapy can be started while a patient is in hospital and carried on systematically after he has come out. This would certainly forestall the necessity of re-entry into hospital for many patients, and ease the pressure on hospitals themselves.

At present, there seems to be little prospect of psychotherapy being developed as an adequately trained speciality. It has many outright opponents, and discussions of the subject, for the most part carried on by those who have only second-hand knowledge of the subject, are full of prejudice. Professor Carstairs ended his fifth Reith Lecture with the words :

'Freud himself, surprised by the vehemence with which his

theories were at first denounced, said that this was because his ideas disturbed the sleep of the world. I believe that it is time that our society awakened to the need for clearer self-knowledge as a means of remedying some of the current disorders in our private and our public life.'

When it really comes to it, however, I do not think that we are any more ready to risk 'clearer self-knowledge' today than in Freud's time. That every *patient* 'resists' treatment by psycho-analysis, i.e. treatment which operates through the acquisition of self-knowledge, was perhaps Freud's most important discovery. Freud knew quite well that it was not, however, only the patients, but also the *doctors* of mankind (using 'doctor' here in its original Greek meaning of 'teacher') who show a strong aversion from knowing themselves, or indeed probing too deeply into the hidden working of the human mind. When people do accept such knowl-edge, it often turns out that the acceptance is more intellectual and conscious than emotional and basic. In fact, the failure so far to develop psychotherapy adequately as a speciality in its own right, is due to a mixture of intellectual, practical and emotional considerations.

The intellectual situation is very clearly put by Professor Car-stairs. He says:

'It is not on logical grounds that medicine has so long resisted psychotherapy. I believe that here we have another instance of events (in this case the series of discoveries about the human mind which were initiated by Sigmund Freud) that out-stripped the grasp of human imagination. We have been living in an era dominated by discoveries in biology and in the physical sciences, discoveries which have brought tremendous changes in our material surroundings. Medicine too has profited by these discoveries . . . but I believe that as a result it has become too exclusively preoccupied with material techniques . . . which are far from being the only valid means of studying the human mind. Even in the practical realm of treating the sick, it may be that the great upsurge of biological research has al-ready made its major contribution. Meanwhile we are neglecting some of the greatest health problems of our contemporary society, the problems of faulty psychological and social adjust-ment.'

The great reluctance shown today by the world of medicine in general, and by not a few prominent psychiatrists in particular, to move purposively beyond the biological into the psychological sphere, has, however, practical as well as intellectual reasons. Psychiatrists are, to a considerable extent, the victims of their situation. They have to operate in an age in which an enormous expansion of our *awareness* of mental ill-health has taken place. The waiting lists for treatment are simply beyond the physical capacity of psychiatrists as a whole to deal with. With this burden of the immediate pressure of cases, they are bound to resist any demands that they should become involved in lengthy psycho-therapeutic treatments. They are bound to fall back on what appear to be the most likely methods of securing a sufficiently speedy improvement to enable the present patient to make way for the next one. The cost, at present, not simply in money but even more in time, of both psychotherapeutic training and psycho-therapeutic treatment, place it out of reach of the majority of both psychiatrists and patients. This, of course, is not a proper reason for rejecting psychotherapy in principle. It must rather be a spur to bring about the far-reaching changes which will have to come before these practical difficulties can be remedied. In the last forty years all that Freud initiated has gained a firm foothold in this country. We can hope that in the next twenty, not only will his work be further developed by the specializing few, but that realistic steps will prove capable of being taken, to make it avail-able in a really adequate way for both training and treatment: so that it will no longer be true, as Professor Carstairs says, that little attention has been paid in Britain to what psychotherapists have been saying 'since the beginning of this century . . . least of all in our great schools of medicine'.

The intellectual and practical difficulties above mentioned do, however, rest on the deeper and more hidden emotional difficulties, and they would probably be easier to overcome but for this subtler influence. The reasons for psychotherapy being such a contro-versial subject are far from being properly scientific. The scientific attitude is not to pick and choose among phenomena and neglect what we do not like, but to get on with investigating everything that confronts us. What does confront us in 'man' is a complex phenomenon which has both a bodily and a mental aspect. It is precisely when we turn from the bodily to the mental aspect of man, from the organism to the person, that this high standard of scientific disinterestedness becomes hard to maintain. In treat-ment, psychotherapy involves coming to close quarters with a sometimes extremely mentally disturbed human being. This may well disturb the personality of the physician. It will usually in-volve taking long-term responsibility for the patient, and not everyone will be prepared to be so tied. A consultant once said to me, 'I wouldn't have your job for all the wealth in the world'. It means working under discouraging conditions. One must be patient, and content to go the patient's pace, and wait for the slow regrowth of a shattered mind back to self-confidence. No authoritarian attitudes, and no attempts to put pressure on the patient, will do other than retard progress. Psychotherapy involves quite peculiar strains that may well break down the physician, which is the reason why the proper training for psychoanalysis involves having an analysis oneself.

It is much easier to be on the defensive against the patient, call the patient difficult, hysteric or unco-operative, adopt a kind of social-moral critical attitude, and prescribe a drug. A young General Practitioner said to me recently, 'I've no patience with neurotics'. I think there is little doubt that fundamentally the hostility to psychotherapy one often comes across, is based on fear of emotional stress wherever found, and this is masked by a pseudo-scientific assumption that all mental disease is bodily caused and ought to be bodily cured. However, the neurotic patient is *never* deceived. He knows quite well whether he is sympathetically understood or not, and those who really need psychotherapeutic help cannot for ever be put off. Ultimately, failure to carry our research in mental ill-health into the region of its true psychological causes may well allow the insidious build up of an explosive situation for society.

2. *The Need for Psychotherapy as a Speciality in its own Right*

The position just outlined, concerning the place of psychotherapy as a controversial subject at the present time, calls for further comment. The lack of a broadly based and widely spread training system makes it difficult to know accurately the real standing of any given psychotherapist. Psychoanalytical literature can be read by any enthusiast who may then feel himself qualified to start practising. I once had a letter from a man who said that his wife suffered from a neurosis and he had made a thorough study of psychoanalytical literature in order to help her. He could not, however, get her to co-operate, and would I write to persuade her to let him analyse her. I replied that he was attempting the impossible, that he had no training in psychotherapy, and that it looked very much as if he wanted intellectually to dominate her; that probably his determination to help her in this way revealed an attitude to her which had a lot to do with causing the outbreak of her neurosis. She no doubt wanted him to be a considerate and affectionate husband and not someone always trying to analyse and explain her. This example may well appear to be an instance of the naïve, but I doubt whether it is any more naïve than the attitude of a General Practitioner who once gave me his opinion that psychoanalysis was no good. He said he had tried it. He had taken an epileptic patient back in memory to her first attacks in childhood and it had made no difference. It did not occur to him that he had no training at all in psychoanalysis and in fact had read very little about it, having only general ideas. He would not have thought of attempting to operate on a patient's body with no more training than that.

In its narrowest sense the term 'psychoanalyst' refers to a fully trained member of one of the national, Freudian, psychoanalytical associations, in this country the British Psychoanalytical Society. The standards of training are very exacting. In addition to this there are trained followers of Carl Jung's *Analytical Psychology* and of Alfred Adler's *Individual Psychology*. Both of these two great figures of the 'pioneer age' of psychodynamic research began work with Freud and separated later to follow their own somewhat different lines. But certainly the main body of 'analytical' research and treatment is Freudian. The theory of psychoanalysis, however, does not stand still where Freud himself left it, and there are today several different schools of thought within the movement, some adhering more to the original and classic theory, others looking ahead to new developments. Perhaps the greatest thing about Freud was the way his own work pointed forward and opened the way for new advances. The phenomenon is familiar in history, of some disciples being more conservative than the great pioneer they follow. Social workers today tend to be trained in a type of Freudian theory which is becoming outdated by further clinical research. No doubt, this kind of time-lag is inevitable.

In addition to these recognized 'schools' of psychodynamic thought, training and therapy, there have also always been a good number of eclectics, often highly skilled, who refused to belong to any school and took whatever they could use from all the schools. Some of the best known of these have been connected with the Tavistock Clinic, founded by Dr. H. Crichton Miller, which carries on both training and treatment. On its staff are to be found therapists of all the schools and of none. Possibly, particularly representative of its independent outlook, was the work of Dr. Ian Suttie whose *Origins of Love and Hate* is a book that made a definite mark and still retains its value. Lastly, we ought to mention some still smaller but significant groups of workers in the field of psychotherapy, such as 'The Open Way' movement led by Dr. Graham Howe, and the Association of Psychotherapists; both run a clinic and also a training programme for therapists. It will be seen from this that training for psychoanalysis and psychotherapy is carried on by essentially private groups of specialists and tends to take the form of 'schools' each with their own individual outlook. It is not yet clear how the move can or will be made to a comprehensive scheme of training in which the medical schools will play their part.

There are some formidable difficulties in the way. One of these is the fact above noted, that psychodynamic theories appear to be the 'property' of 'schools of thought' in which the work of the great pioneers is preserved. This undoubtedly makes for conservatism, for a reluctance to admit the extent to which the founder's work slowly becomes outdated so that some brake is put on theoretical progress. It is often said that psychoanalysts have an emotional vested interest in their own theory; however, in so far as that is true, it is also every bit as true of the opponents of psychoanalysis. The fact has to be faced squarely that it is impossible to preserve quite the same strictly scientific objectivity and neutrality about theories of the human personality as it is about things like atoms and stars, or even newts and body cells. The fact that emotional considerations, however vehemently they may be disowned, enter into the reasons for accepting any kind of psychological, or psychobiological, or psychophysiological theory, is as obvious in the case of the materialistic psychiatrist, the behaviourist, the 'new learning theory' experimental psychologist, as it may be with any psychotherapist. This in itself does not make it easy to take up *the psychodynamic study of the personality* into the permanent structure of the teaching of the medical schools. Schools of thought are not, of course, non-existent in physical medicine but they do not there have quite the same dynamic importance as they have in psychotherapy.

Let us suppose that a Professor of Psychotherapy were to be appointed in every medical school alongside the Professor of Psychiatry. There is an exceedingly strong case, and it will become stronger as time goes on, for treating psychotherapy as a fully distinct speciality in its own right in that way. But is the Professor of Psychotherapy to be a Freudian, Jungian, Adlerian or an Eclectic, and if an eclectic, where is the man with the necessary qualifications to be found? Numerically considered the Freudians would have the best right. The British Psychoanalytical Society is part of a world-wide psychoanalytical organization which holds regular international congresses, and publishes an International

Journal of Psychoanalysis along with other research media. Research is unceasing, and is directly based on therapeutic practice. Numerically, in Britain, though it is the largest of the psychotherapeutic organizations, it numbers only some two hundred and fifty members and associate members, of whom fifty live abroad (in U.S.A., Canada, Australia, S. Africa, India, etc.). Within this organization there are healthy and vigorous differences of opinion, broadly as between the more orthodox and the progressive, which serve as a stimulus to theoretical progress. Also since the last war, there has been more of an attempt by Freudians and Jungians to discover common ground. But we are far from having a broad and increasing field of psychodynamic research which is all-inclusive, free from secretarianism in its primary devotion to scientific progress, and capable of producing the type of workers who might become Professors of Psychotherapy, if and when such posts are created.

The term 'psychotherapist' actually includes those who practice by non-analytical methods, such as suggestion, hypnosis, re-educative techniques and so on, but the day has certainly come when 'psychotherapy' must now be considered to indicate mainly a practice based on a broadly psychoanalytical technique; the other types of psychotherapy can never now be more than incidental or auxiliary. In a purely scientific sense, the term 'psychoanalysis' should refer to a method rather than a school. Where matters of pure theory are concerned, it is in every way preferable to refer to 'psychodynamic science' rather than 'psychoanalysis'. Freud has the sole real claim to be considered the true founder of modern psychodynamic science, but a science cannot be a monopoly nor can it be restricted to the tenets of the man who founds it. In spite of this, there is historical necessity for the psychoanalytical organization to be in a sense exclusive, and I do not think anyone who appreciates the slow way in which important movements must develop historically would wish it to be otherwise. There would have been grave danger of Freud's distinctive insights being lost in a welter of speculation if he had thrown his initial organization open to all and sundry. The interests of progress may well be still best served by this work being carried on by a closely knit group with high standards of membership, and of training. We may, in spite of the fact that such a situation favours an unscientific dogmatism, regard this movement as historically charged with the task of laying the foundations of the ultimate 'speciality of psychotherapy' which must arise.

A second reason for the difficulty in passing from the stage of 'schools' to that of a broadly based psychodynamic science, capable of general training schemes in which the medical schools could play a part, is of a different kind, and we shall not elaborate it extensively at this point. As we proceed, however, with the examination of all the problems thrown up by psychotherapy, it will become obvious that it goes far beyond narrowly medical concerns. It is doubtful if problems of the 'personality' as such can be called primarily medical at all. They are at least just as much a direct concern for education, social science, ethical philosophy, and religion. Many and varied disciplines can rightly claim to have a finger in this pie. It is probably due only to the fact that personality disorders tend markedly to produce bodily tensions and physical symptoms, that this field of personality disorder has been first radically explored from the medical standpoint, in the early work of the hypnotists (Charcot and Janet in particular) and Freud. Since then, psychoanalysis has proved to be highly relevant to many non-medical lines of study and today is widely made use of in sociology, philosophy, education, trained social case-work, and even cautiously by some religious thinkers, though far more enthusiastically and not seldom intemperately in literature. However, all this shows that psychodynamic science is not a narrowly medical concern; it is literally a 'science of the personality-dynamics of human living'. In their textbook of Psychiatry, Mayer-Gross, Slater and Roth deplore the tendency to separate psychiatric issues from medicine; and certainly that would be a mistake. However, they seem to betray the opposite tendency to resist the fact that personality problems cannot be restricted to the field of medicine. This no doubt constitutes a difficulty in the way of including psychotherapy as a speciality in its own right, within the field of medical training. The time is probably not yet ripe for the solution of this problem.

At this point a question arises which at present is very difficult to handle wisely. The suggestion of a Professor of Psychotherapy, alongside or distinct from a Professor of Psychiatry, emphasizes the fact that 'psychiatry' and 'psychotherapy' are to a very considerable extent separate things. They ought never to be allowed to part company, but they are not at all necessarily identical, and are not at the present time very effectively married. A psychiatrist is not usually in any specialized sense trained in psychotherapy. He usually acquires a certain amount of facility in short-term psychotherapy in the course of his work, though this depends on his own temperament and outlook. Naturally, some psychiatrists discover a high degree of natural aptitude and develop great psychotherapeutic skill without any other training than their own innate ability to learn by experience. Of these Freud himself was one, for there was no one to analyse him. One could mention such an outstanding psychiatrist as the American Harry Stack Sullivan, who had a genius for understanding schizophrenics, and developed a thoroughly psychodynamic outlook which he called 'The Interpersonal Theory of Psychiatry'. The point is that it is an entirely individual matter whether the psychiatrist chooses out of his own keenness to specialize in psychotherapy or not. I do not see that any exception can be taken to that, so long as the position is frankly understood that a doctor is not necessarily a psychotherapist in a trained and specialized sense because he is a psychiatrist. At present it cannot be otherwise since no widely available specialized training in psychotherapy exists.

Psychotherapy is and ought to be an exacting speciality in its own right. There is a dangerous tendency at present to think of it as a medical auxiliary discipline like dentistry, but this is not adequate to the facts, for it reaches beyond the borders of medicine into many sides of life. Both psychotherapy and the psychodynamic theory on which it must rest, aim to understand and promote the full development to maturity of the whole personality, and it would be an unrealistic limitation if such a discipline were restricted to any one professional interest, be it medical, sociological, educational or religious. Contributors from all these fields of study are necessary to the fullest understanding of human living. In so far as disturbed personality may often involve illness, psychotherapy must be carried on in full and close association with medicine, but disturbed personality just as often involves not illness but crime and delinquency, marital disharmony, bad parental handling of children, inability to make easy relationships with other people in social or business activities. I once had a patient come for analysis solely on the ground that hitherto he had worked in his laboratory and been happy but now he was promoted to an executive position and found himself severely limited by his shy and inhibited personality. In the attempt at the psychotherapy of 'character problems' where no question of illness has arisen, it may still turn out that in the process of dealing with the deep-seated anxieties that are the cause of the pure personality-problem, the patient may begin to put up the automatic defences of that kind of repression that drives undischarged tensions into the body and so leads to a disturbance of physical well-being. This does not always happen in dealing with 'character problems' but the fact that it may and often does happen shows that it is necessary for psychotherapy, however far-flung its extra-medical concerns may be, to keep close touch with medicine as well. The fact is that we are increasingly having to recognize that a human being is a whole who cannot be conveniently split up among a number of different 'specialities' who know nothing of each other's work and want to have a monopoly of some fictitious 'section' of human nature. Psychotherapy must then be developed as a speciality in its own right, and at the same time keep close touch with medicine on the one hand and all kinds of social and educational work on the other. This is what brought into being the Psychiatric Social Worker. Also today, for example, Probation Officers are trained to understand the psychodynamic approach, and no type of trained social work now omits instruction to some extent in psychodynamic concepts. They are included in the curriculum of the course for Educational Psychologists. The day will certainly come when Theological Colleges will not be able to afford to be left behind in this matter, though it must be said that hitherto Freudian psychology has not had much that was constructive to offer to the theologian. The only clear-cut case I know of, where the attempt was made to correlate the two, was the use of Freud's instinct theory to support the doctrine of original sin, by Professor N. P. Williams. Recent psychodynamic developments have something much more valuable to offer than that. Professor Reinhold Niebuhr, the great American theologian, Professor Tillich, and in this country the Rev. A. H. Williams (Dean of Trinity College), one of the group of Cambridge theologians at present challenging attention, are examples of theologians well versed in psychoanalysis. It would be equally a tragedy if psychodynamic studies and psychotherapy ever became exclusively either medical or nonmedical, and fortunately there is no possibility of that. The complexity of human problems will force into ever closer cooperation all those who are concerned to understand them and to help.

This position calls for a revision of terms. Freud discussed the question of what was then called 'Lay-Analysis' or 'Lay Therapy', and he made it clear that he did not accept the limitation of psychoanalysis to the medical profession as desirable. He stated that much of a doctor's training has no bearing on the understanding of 'personality' as such, and in fact such training may give a materialistic bias which hinders the appreciation of psychological facts. This will be largely a matter of individual type of mind and temperament. Within the psychoanalytic movement, many of the important contributors have been non-medical, such as Miss Anna Freud, Mrs. Melanie Klein, Ernst Kris, Erik Erikson and others, and this has always been accepted. What was insisted on was specialized training. In considering the term 'Lay Therapist', it may be observed that the *Concise Oxford Dictionary* defines the term 'lay' as meaning 'non-expert'; i.e. 'layman, one of the laity, non-expert in regard to some profession, art or science'. The term 'lay therapist' could then be applied to a doctor practising psychotherapy when untrained for it, but not to a non-medical man who has had a full training for just this kind of work.

The main point I am driving at in all this is of great importance. The early pioneer phase in which psychotherapy arose as a kind of side-growth on the body of medicine, always uneasily related to and never very fully accepted by the parent body, has now passed away. We may well ask why the kind of psychological discoveries of which Freud was the great pioneer were not made in the field of criminology and education where they have so much relevance. The reason why they were not is not only that there are far more ill people than criminals, and that education was too exclusively intellectually orientated. It was the original medical setting which permitted Freud to make these discoveries because it is only the relief of suffering which sustains people to explore themselves. In fact, an astonishing amount of what psychoanalysis has put forth in technical terms is to be found embedded in the writings of medieval religious mystics, and to a lesser extent in the work of the great novelists, two spheres where concern with suffering is inescapable; what was lacking here was the scientific urge to systematic investigation and formulation. But *today, the pioneer stage is passing and psychodynamic science must become a distinct and separate speciality in its own right, along with its application in psychotherapy.* There is nothing in the whole range of human living that it does not bear on.

Human beings in general tend to assume that they understand human nature as a matter of course, of natural common sense. One of the tragic applications of this in practice is the general idea that anyone can be a parent, whether or not they have taken any trouble to understand children. A parallel assumption is that anyone of experience can be a 'psychotherapist' or is qualified to pass judgement in this field. But training in medicine or theology or education does not make a psychotherapist. I am far from wanting to enslave people's judgement to experts in any field. Experts are quite often wrong, but that does not make non-experts infallibly right, and there are advantages in giving a lifetime to the special study of one important branch of knowledge. The time is now overdue for this to be *generally* recognized as true for the understanding of the dynamics of the human mind. This is a difficult and complex study, and must come to be accepted as a special field of research and training and practice in its own right, and one that should be open to all serious workers in human welfare.

I do not think that, at present, this question is an easy one to settle, partly owing to the fact already noted that there are as yet too many different schools of thought in psychodynamic science. We have not yet outgrown the confusion of the early pioneer stage, and it would be by no means easy at present to lay down an accepted body of psychodynamic theory which a medical school, for example, might teach as a basis for practical training in psychotherapy. But I have little doubt that in time this will cease to be true. Psychoanalysis has as yet had only a very short history compared with other sciences, and there are important signs that more and more fundamental facts about the way human personality functions are becoming clearer. One is rather looking to the future for the development of a truly comprehensive and humanly widely based speciality of psychodynamic research and of psychotherapy, to remedy the unsatisfactory situation which obtains today so far as the part played by psychotherapy in dealing with mental ill-health is concerned.

The question I am often asked: 'How does one become a psychotherapist?' is thus not easy to answer at present. I think it would be very generally agreed that one ought not to seek to specialize in psychotherapy at too early an age. It is essential first to acquire some real experience of life by pursuing one of the professions directly concerned with human beings and their problems. Such professions would be medicine, social work, education and religion. Probably not earlier than the age of thirty, it would then be necessary to have a thorough personal training analysis together with instructional courses. But it is clear from our survey of the existing situation that at present the provision of adequate training for suitable candidates for psychotherapy from various professions, is grossly insufficient to meet the widespread need of the massive problem of mental ill-health, so long as it is only obtainable in London and from a few small specialist organizations. It is not impossible, but very difficult, for a determined individual to secure a personal analysis for training purposes outside London, for the simple reason that there are very few trained analysts outside London to go to, and, once again, the cost of analytic training is a great deterrent. We are only in the infancy of psychotherapy as a properly trained speciality, and no doubt the future will see big developments in this matter. Meanwhile, it is as difficult for medically trained people as for non-medicals to come by a full training for this work. It is hard for anyone in the thirties (the best time), usually with a family, to uproot himself and start on a further course of training. Hence the need for future organizational developments if psychotherapy is ever to play its proper part in the battle for a healthy-minded population.

3. What is Psychotherapy?

We have so far been discussing what might be called the practical and political problems of psychotherapy as a highly trained speciality, without giving more than a brief indication of what it is. A preliminary description of psychotherapy was given on pages 87 and 115, bringing out the importance of the relationship between the therapist and the patient, and this was further emphasized on page 119 by a reference to the emotional strains that psychotherapy involves for the therapist. These will obviously have a great bearing on his ability to provide a 'therapeutic relationship' for the patient. At this point, therefore, it will be well to state what is involved in the nature and practice of psychotherapy, a statement which will then be filled out increasingly as we go on to consider its critics, and its difficulties in detail.

A favourite slogan with those who oppose psychotherapy is that 'pills are better than pep talks', which shows how little some people know about psychotherapy. If there is one thing that psychotherapy is not, it is pep talk. One might say that pep talk is a kind of 'common-sense psychotherapy', and is always the first kind used. It represents in the main an impatient wish on the part of the pep-talker that the mentally ill person should be able to deny his difficulties and behave in a way more convenient to other people. Pep talk may be moral. 'Don't be so selfish, you should forget yourself and think more of others, and get down to some steady hard work.' That was said recently to a patient who was breaking down into serious depression. It may be religious pep talk. 'You should have more faith in God'. But, as one patient said, 'No one tells me how to have faith when I feel in despair, and feel I can't trust anyone or anything'. It may be medical pep talk. 'My doctor says I must pull myself together. He says I am letting myself go to pieces and the cure is in my own hands. He says I should take these tablets and get out and about more and stop brooding.' Then the patient usually adds, 'I've been struggling to do all that for years and I feel I can't go on without help; and anyway how do I stop brooding?'

Let us suppose that at this point it is realized that pep talk is useless. The patient's illness *consists* in the fact that his personality is somehow really damaged so that he is not capable, beyond a certain point, of taking all that advice. Let us suppose that recourse to drugs or E.C.T. have been found to give temporary relief but no lasting cure, and he is then fortunate enough to find his way to a trained psychotherapist. What happens then? In the first place, the patient is not subjected to a battery of questions. He is left free to tell his own story. He is not hurried because the important things are the most painful to talk about. Such information as the therapist needs he can wait for. What is on the patient's own mind right here and now is more important. Slowly, without pressure, he is helped to unfold the story of his mental distress, to a patient and sympathetic listener. This listener will carefully explain back to the patient as much as he feels can be accepted at a time, of the significance of what the patient is saying. Gradually this very emotionally disturbed person begins to understand himself in a new way. He ceases to feel he is just an inexplicable and puzzling mass of problems. He begins to become more and more free, in this new secure human relationship, to allow his personality to regrow in a natural manner. While the new insight is essential, it is only in this 'therapeutic relationship' that it can be either achieved or used.

Thus, *in psychotherapy, the therapist-patient relationship is the key to the nature and success of the treatment.* It is different from the relationship of the physician, and in many respects of the psychiatrist, to the patient. They are seeking information in order to arrive at a diagnosis as soon as may be, and then to prescribe medicines or some other form of treatment. Even then one can't altogether ignore the impact of the doctor's personality on the patient. Ill people are of necessity frightened, and fear hinders the smooth working of the mind. If a bad impact is made, the patient gets more frightened and then the doctor won't get all the information he needs as accurately as he wants it. A patient of mine who had seen a psychiatrist said, 'He questioned me till I felt I'd scream under the pressure, and he gave me no chance to tell him what I felt most worried about'. Then she added, 'You hardly ever ask me a question'. I pointed out that the psychiatrist's job at that stage was to make a diagnosis and recommendation for treatment, but that I, as a psychotherapist, had a quite different job to do.

Again, we may ask, 'What is the psychotherapist's job?' Just as it is not pep talk, so it is not just to comfort and sympathize with a frightened person. That plays its part but by itself would lead to stalemate. Even at a very simple level it is the 'atmosphere' of the interview that enables the patient to talk about the real problems, and the accurate understanding of the therapist that opens the way for progress to be made with them. While the more serious and developed personality illnesses require specialist treatment, it would be a mistake to think that only specialist psychotherapy is of any use. Dr. Balint, in London, is pioneering seminars for groups of General Practitioners, to enable them to make a more psychodynamic approach to their patients' illnesses. I have had a number of General Practitioners as patients over the years, and they have all reported that as they progressed themselves in their analysis, they became much more understanding and sympathetic, and were more effective, in their work with their own patients in anxiety-states. There is a great deal of 'preventive psychotherapy' to be done at this level, which can save bad breakdowns.

It must not be assumed, however, that once an understanding psychotherapist provides a sympathetic atmosphere, it is then all plain sailing and the patient has only to talk and get well. If the patient could respond as easily as that he would not be ill. As has been shown in Parts 1 and 2, he is divided against himself, this being the essence of his internal conflicts. The result is that he gets into difficulties in so many of his personal relationships because his own internal divisions make him divided and inconsistent in his reactions to other people. Then when he comes to a psychotherapist, it is just this kind of trouble that he reproduces in relation to his analyst. He both wants his help and wants to do without him; it is a sign that the treatment situation becomes real, when the patient finds himself reproducing in his reactions to the therapist all the problems he finds himself enmeshed in, in his ordinary life. Only by 'living' every conflict *inside the treatment situation* can he gain the opportunity to grow out of his internal contradictions. The analyst must become involved, from the patient's point of view, in all his conflicts of love versus hate, dependence versus independence, the need for security versus the longing for freedom, the relapse back into the helplessness of the frightened child versus the struggle to keep going as the capable adult. At each stage the patient has genuine needs that the therapist must understand and meet. One of the most important of these is a constant one, the need for the therapist to be capable of entering into all the stress and strain of the patient's conflicts without being personally involved in such a way as would lead to his being dragged down with the patient into mental chaos.

The psychotherapist who uses the psychoanalytical method must be able to give the patient a perfectly real relationship which remains the one stable factor through all the patient's fluctuating moods. It must be a relationship in which the patient feels a genuine and not a simulated sympathy, which begets the kind of patience and persistence which enables the patient to discover that after each emotional crisis, however difficult it has been, the relationship is still there as the enduring foundation of his hope of a 'cure'. The therapist must understand the patient, but that does not mean that he must pretend always to understand, whether he does or not. The patient knows at once when he is not being understood, and cannot accept anything false being put across on him. Particularly patients resent anything that looks like 'fitting them into a theory'. They need to be understood as individuals in their own right. The therapist, naturally, is not omniscient and infallible, and the patient will respect him if he says at some point, 'I don't understand yet exactly what is happening to you, but I'm seeking to understand and together we will find out what it's all about'. Gradually, really meaningful and trustful mutual communication must come about, out of which the patient can be lifted from his slough of despond, his despairing puzzlement about himself.

It seems probable that a lot of misunderstanding has arisen as a result of vague popular notions of Freud's theory of 'transference' coupled with his theory of the Oedipus Complex. The patient is held to repeat on the analyst all his early love-fixations, as well as his hates, and one often hears reference to 'patients falling in love with the analyst', as if this were the same kind of thing as is meant by 'falling in love' in the adult sense. I am bound to say that in over twenty years I have never come upon anything like that, nor do I believe it will be met if the position is clearly established that the therapist-patient relationship is basically, as to its emotional pattern, a parent-child relation. Therein lies the difficulty of the patient's being able to accept treatment. It is hard to admit that one's problems are due to the fact that some part of one's personality still carries the legacy of childhood so literally, that one actually feels and reacts as a child in that part of oneself. Patients usually struggle to hold on to an adult level of functioning during sessions, and when the child's starved need for love is aroused, this may be disguised as if it were an adult love for the analyst; a kind of love, however, which soon reveals its childhood origins by bringing hate in its train because of the fear of dependence. Such love must be interpreted so as to be resolved back into its underlying reality, the child's need for security in a personal relationship, without which he cannot 'find himself'. A simple illustration of this may be given. A young married woman came into session in an exhausted state and lay down thankfully on the couch to rest. However, she could not relax but fidgeted about. When I asked what was the matter, she said that she was afraid that if she relaxed she would start wanting me to have sexual intercourse with her. I said, with a good deal of knowledge of her problems, that I did not think that was her real trouble at all. She was afraid that if she really relaxed her struggle to keep going, she would begin to feel like a frightened, helpless infant, and the prospect of feeling like that in my presence scared her. She at once became calm and silent and restful, and presently said, 'You're right. What I'm afraid of is being a baby and looking silly.' Appearances of wanting adult relationships with the therapist, other than normal and appropriate ones, is a defence to be seen through.

Yet there is an adult relationship that the patient can expect to develop with the therapist, which is more than that of seeking and paying for professional advice. As patient and therapist come to understand one another, to whatever degree they have any real affinity and capacity for mutual appreciation, a straightforward feeling of friendship can develop. Perhaps not till that does develop can the 'cure' become at all complete. It will be the kind of friendship that ought to grow between parents and developing children, so that at last when the child leaves home, he is strong enough to stand on his own feet, able to feel an adult *on the level* of his parents, and retaining a sense of security from having parents in the background who can be relied on to be understanding. The psychotherapist-patient relationship is a parent-child relationship inside a maturing adult friendly one, and this shows the more clearly the deeper the treatment goes.

It must, however, be said that not all psychotherapy is on the same level. Just as there are different levels of treatment in the broad psychiatric sense, so there are different levels of psychotherapy. I shall distinguish three. These three different levels of psychotherapy are determined by what the patient wants, what therapeutic goal he is aiming at. We assume, in accordance with what has been said, that the patient and the therapist have enough in common, and a sufficient natural ability to understand each other, to make reasonable intelligent co-operation and a natural degree of friendly relationship possible. Then, what the psychotherapist has to do for the patient depends on what the patient is seeking. Not all patients by any means want a thoroughgoing and radical psychoanalysis. To suggest it at first, even when it is really necessary, may only frighten the patient off. It may well be that at first the patient does not clearly know what he wants, and one may have to wait a bit and give him time to find out. To decide, he may need more understanding of himself than at first he possesses. The idea that from the very first the patient is committed to 'the analytic couch' and plunged into 'deep psycho-analysis' is unrealistic. If treatment develops into that, it is because the patient comes to see that nothing short of radical treatment will meet his needs. It may be said in passing, that 'the couch' is not today the invariable condition of psychoanalysis that it once was. My own experience is that patients make use of the couch if and when that helps them most. The therapist must above all not adopt an authoritarian attitude of telling the patient what to do.

Since the fundamental difficulty is the conflict in the patient between his need to seek help and his intensely strong feeling of being ashamed of needing it and trying to make himself be independent and do without it, this is the main thing the psycho-therapist must understand. He needs to sense accurately the patient's state of feeling and make the response appropriate to that. At one time the patient will be prepared to depend and be helped and at such a time, if intense anxiety is emerging, he may want extra sessions. At another time he may be feeling a powerful urge towards regaining independence, and then it may well be a good thing to agree to dropping a session. The same oscillation will take place as between the use of the couch and the use of a chair or even sitting on the floor or standing to talk. What is essential is that, whatever way the patient reacts its inner significance must be understood, and the patient helped to gain insight into it. This goes for the length of treatment. If the patient wishes to end treatment at a certain point, all that needs to be done is to make sure he knows why. It may actually be a good thing for a patient to stop after having made an initial improvement, and discover for himself, if he feels a need to, whether he must go deeper. If he does, he will do it with much more conviction and make better use of the treatment. We may now briefly consider the three main levels on which treatment is likely to be carried on. I will call these the treatment of symptoms, the treatment of conflicts in human relationships, and the treat-ment of the basic personality-problem, the arrest of ego-develop-ment.

Symptom-Treatment

Sometimes it proves possible to clear up a symptomatic dis-turbance of sexual functioning quite quickly. So far as my ex-perience goes, when a sexual symptom cannot be relinquished quickly once its meaning and motivation are clear, then it usually proves to be deeply entangled in complex character-problems and does not clear up till far-reaching changes have matured. Thus, a patient once came to me complaining of premature ejaculation. In the space of six sessions he came to understand that he suffered from a kind of premature ejaculation in everything. He was impulsive to an extraordinary degree, rushed into decisions without thinking sufficiently about them in his business, was easily diverted from anything he was doing, and would fly off at a tangent pouring energy and interest into something that caught his fancy before he tired of it. I pointed out to him that this was the pattern of his sexual life as well. He had never thought of seeing his sexual reactions as an expression of his personality, but regarded sex as a purely physical function. He said that his premature ejaculation was already markedly improved, and he stopped treatment, saying that he would certainly come back if the trouble recurred. He did not come back. That does not prove that the trouble did not recur, but he was satisfied at the time of ceasing that he had overcome this trouble. It is possible that even this short treatment initiated a new attitude in him towards himself which could have beneficial results.

Another male patient complained of impotence, and within a dozen sessions unfolded a story of the hurt of a broken marriage with its aftermath of depression. This had been a shock to him and he had 'gone into his shell' until at last he felt that he must do something about this, and resume a normal life again. He presently became friendly with a girl and discovered to his dismay that he was quite devoid of any sexual feelings for her. He concluded that he had become impotent. It was only necessary to point out that the shock of his broken marriage had given him a 'once bitten, twice shy' attitude which was far stronger unconsciously than he realized. He could not risk releasing any real emotion again for a woman, or he might become involved once more and risk another repetition of his former hurt. Having come to see how he was feeling, he faced the whole problem realistically and stopped treatment, satisfied that he could now risk a friendship without undue anxiety and get over his difficulty.

In a different type of case, a woman was having what she believed to be 'heart attacks' so severe that she would collapse in the street. Her doctor could find nothing wrong with her heart and sent her for analysis. It took about twenty sessions to bring the situation under control. The problem was that this woman was still living at home with a violent-tempered father of whom she was terrified. Every day as she was returning from work, she would get more and more anxious as to how she would find him when she got in. Palpitation of the heart would accompany this mounting anxiety and then, believing that she had a bad heart, her anxiety would become ever more intensified. She learned to stop when she felt this symptom coming on, and remind herself that she was getting frightened and that her heart was quite all right. She could then face her fears more consciously and the collapses in the street ceased. This short analysis did not so much 'cure' her symptom, as enable her to accept it for what it was and not work it up into something terrifying. Analysis could not cure her of anxiety, for it could not cure her of father.

Treatment of Conflicts in Human Relationships

The material dealt with at this level of treatment is of the kind described in Chapter 3, the classic Oedipal or family pattern of personal relationships. This is the Freudian analysis *par excellence*. The complex human relationships in which the patient shared as a child in his family group, repeatedly prove to be deeply embedded in his mental make-up, acting as secret determinants of his relationships with quite other people in his grown-up life. Talking out the conscious and unconscious repressed elements in his disturbed relations with the people he lives and works with, and tracing them back to their origins in his early life, allows a gradual reorganization of his personality to take place. Blind repression, resulting in ill-understood and disturbed sexual and aggressive reactions, comes to be slowly replaced by less pathological mental controls. The result may be either a more normal obsessional character, conscientious and hardworking but no longer fanatically so, or else a more normal schizoid character, sufficiently detached to avoid the risk of getting too stirred up emotionally (i.e. 'not wearing his heart on his sleeve') but yet for that very reason more able to mix with people with less anxiety. These results are really a compromise between the need and the fear of human relations, but many patients are able to stabilize at this compromise solution, and live a happier life without pursuing analysis to the bitter end. Indeed with some patients it would be far harder, if not impossible, to take them deeper into their unconscious and repressed basic insecurity, than to support their need to call a halt at that stage.

Treatment of the Basic Personality Problem, Arrested Ego-Development

Here we have to sift the trouble to rock bottom. Professor Carstairs referred to mental health problems as 'problems of faulty psychological and social adjustment'. This, I feel, gives an inadequate account of the deepest roots of mental illness. The idea of 'adjustment' implies a more or less normal 'capacity' to adjust to the stresses and strains of adult living, and when mental illness is seen in terms of 'maladjustment' only, it conjures up a picture of a personality which is all right in itself but has somehow got into bad relationships with its environment; this has only to be sorted out and the patient can readjust himself and all is well. Some such view as that has in fact, I believe, been the cause of much of the pessimism about poor results of psychotherapy in the past. It has not been realized how deep-seated the trouble lies. Problems of faulty adjustment belong to the previous level of conflicts over human relationships. Whenever these are too severe, their investigation ultimately leads down into far profounder problems, which involve nothing short of the basic soundness of the personality as a whole, the fundamental strength, not innate strength but developmental strength, of the ego, the core of the personal self. It is because of this that the more ill the patient is, the more one is constantly confronted with his sense of weakness, inadequacy, inferiority, even nonentity and unreality.

I particularly stressed that this is an ego-weakness which is not due to any innate, hereditary deficiency. Patients of obviously great abilities and great natural force of personality can suffer from these frightening feelings of utter inability to cope with life. What they lack is not due to any biological failure to give them the necessary raw material of a vigorous self; it is due to the obstruction and arrest of processes of development in their earliest years, which ought to have made possible the full use of their natural powers instead of blocking it. I often point out to patients when they feel despairing, that their illness, though it is due to things that went wrong at very early stages of their post-natal life, is still not the deepest nor the ultimate thing in them. They can get well because they have a primary, vigorous nature, possessing all the normal capacities for feeling, interest and activity, and only waiting for the chance of free development as their fears are overcome. A healthy nature lies hidden behind the illness. This is often expressed by saying that even in psychosis there is a healthy part of the personality watching over the whole process. This, again, is what Dr. Winnicott referred to when he expressed the view already mentioned, that when an infant cannot find the right environment in which his personality could develop properly, he puts his true self in cold storage to await a more favourable opportunity of psychological rebirth.

This is not a question of readjustment but of fundamental regrowth. A too seriously injurious infancy and childhood, as we saw in Part 2, actually arrests and distorts the basic development of the personality as an emotional whole. The foundations of a secure, naturally strong, non-anxious, friendly, humane and self-confident personality are not laid. Ever afterwards life is a desperate struggle to try to force oneself to feel equal to doing what one knows one can do all the time, without ever feeling any confidence or happy enjoyment about one's activity. These feelings can and do occur to patients on all levels of psychotherapy. The most ill patients have no choice but to trace them to their source with someone who can understand it all, and stand by them while they grow out of their 'slough of despond'.

Thus an extremely able patient intellectually, once said to me: 'My terrible problem is of what I'm going to do with my life. I feel I need someone to tell me what I ought to do. Suicide would be better than living on a low level, a liability to the community.' A professional man doing valuable work for the community said: 'I'm most vulnerable in group discussions. I feel that if I just sit back and listen and relax, I'll fade out altogether. At times I'm appalled at the strength of my feelings of panic if I can't contribute to a discussion. People will see through me, will crack my façade and see I'm a nobody.' Behind this feeling of the non-existence of a stable core of the personality, there always lies a tragic story of childhood, either of active terrorization or else of more subtle undermining, emotional neglect, and failure to provide for the child the human relations in which alone a real personal self can grow. The legacy of those early years is still alive and active deep within the unconscious, and its results are manifest in everyday conscious living as chronic tension and self-forcing.

Treatment of this deepest level problem is necessarily long, often very long, and any attempt to speed it up only makes matters worse, for that is exactly what the patient has been trying to do all his life. According to Dr. Winnicott, treatment ultimately has to involve a 'therapeutic regression', a going back to the beginning under the control of the analysis, in order to initiate a rebirth and regrowth of the personality in a fundamental way. Is this possible? I shall come back to this question in the last chapter, but I will here only say that my own experience is that it is possible. Moreover the longest and hardest part of the process is not the regrowing, but the taking of the risk of 'going backwards'. It is so often felt that it will mean risking the total loss of the adult personality, but when at last the patient can, by slow stages, get back to the real roots of his anxieties and ego-weakness, even if, as in some few cases happens, it involves a temporary 'breakdown' into 'incapacitating illness', that proves to be the opening of the door to real recovery. I have seen this happen to four patients in the last two years, and all are doing better now than they have ever done in their lives. I do not minimize the difficulties of treatment of this ultimate level. We know all too little about it as yet, but of its possibility I have no doubt. Perhaps it is in this problem of 'therapeutic regression' that we have most need of close co-operation between the hospital and the psychoanalytical therapist, but it is by no means true that treatment even of this radical kind must inevitably involve hospitalization.

This account of psychotherapy leaves so much to be said, and raises so many questions at every turn, that we must take a look in the next chapter, before we go further, at the critics of psychotherapy, as a means of highlighting and clarifying some of the major issues involved. This chapter may, therefore, be rounded off with a few general observations. It will be seen that deep psychoanalysis *aims* at a radical cure. Even though it may not yet be able reliably to produce, or in many cases, even to approach, this perfectionist result, its research aims at the ever-deepening understanding that may make approximation to that result more possible. Degrees of treatment will vary with degrees of illness, but there are few cases of so-called nervous illness where the patient could not benefit from some degree of psychotherapy, if he is at all the type of person who could make use of it. This type of treatment, however, except in the case of symptom-treatment, is not very well suited to public clinics, being better carried on · in a quiet and more private atmosphere; and it is not specifically provided for under the National Health Service. Before that might become possible, great changes of outlook and administration will have to come about. It is relevant to observe that it is not possible to psychoanalyse a person 'in spite of himself'. He cannot merely be 'sent' for analysis, and if he comes freely out of his own conviction, he still needs to have a say in his choice of psychotherapist. He cannot be automatically 'allotted' to any therapist with a maximum chance of success. This kind of problem is not impossible to overcome where the psychiatrist who diagnoses, and recommends analysis, understands both the personality of the patient and of the possible therapists available, so that a good 'matching' of personalities is feasible. These considerations, however, show some of the difficulties facing attempts at provision of genuine psychotherapy on a large scale.

It should be mentioned that research and experiment go on to find effective means of adapting psychoanalysis to short-term treatment, as in the work of Dr. F. Alexander and his team at the Chicago Institute of Psychoanalysis; and also to find means of spreading this kind of treatment to make it more widely applicable, as in the experiment of group therapy. In this, a small selected group of patients talk out their problems with one another, including their reactions to one another in the group, while a psychotherapist 'sits in' with the group and gives interpretative comments where necessary. It would seem that such treatment cannot reach the depths of ordinary psychoanalysis, but that is not necessary for everyone, and good enough results have accrued to make this an increasingly widely tried method. Much work of this kind is being done at the Tavistock Clinic in London, and group therapy is being tried in many hospitals and clinics. I have recently read in manuscript an account of a group therapy experiment carried out in Aberdeen by Dr. F. A. MacNab (now of Victoria, Australia) with male schizophrenic patients, which produced very significant therapeutic results. No doubt the future will see many experiments in psychotherapy, yet in the end it seems unlikely that there can be any final substitute for the thorough, prolonged investigation of an individual personality if the deepest problems are to be solved.

One last point may here be mentioned. It is often claimed that if nervous illnesses are left to themselves, a spontaneous self-cure will sooner or later result. Indeed, an acute outbreak of any form of anxiety-illness will moderate after a time, say within a period of six months to two years. One of the factors in this is a parallel to what Freud called 'The Psychopathology of Everyday Life', namely 'The Psychotherapy of Everyday Life'. A human being is a living creature, and to be alive means not to be stagnant. We do not stand still. If we are not degenerating and going downhill, then, however slowly and imperceptibly, we will be moving forward, and growing. But the apparent 'self-cures' are nevertheless deceptive. They turn out to be repressions rather than cures of the illness. Many people have a history of repeated breakdown at intervals of three to five years over periods of anything up to thirty and forty years. Each particular 'attack' after a time subsides, but unless something has been done to make some real difference to the personality as a whole, it is only a matter of time in most cases before some further pressure in real life will trigger off another 'breakdown'. The period of breakdown is the right time to turn to psychotherapy. In the last resort it is the elimination of FEAR that is required, for it is fear that creates hate, makes love impossible and shuts people up within themselves. It is increasingly the view today that the psychotherapist helps a person to achieve a durable change for the better, if he is able to bring a belated but genuine equivalent of parental love to bear on the deepest hidden fears and hurts of the patient and restore him to what I might call 'confidence in depth'. This is by no means easy to translate into terms of treatment, and the challenge it constitutes for the psychotherapist is that, in the end, it is more a matter of what he *is*, than of what he says and does. Professor Carl Rogers (Wisconsin University) writes:

'Can I be in some way that will be perceived by the other person as trustworthy, dependable or consistent in some deep sense. . . . The degree to which I can create relationships which facilitate the growth of others as separate persons, is a measure of the growth I have achieved myself*.

* *Characteristics of a Helping Relationship*, Canada's Mental Health Supplement, 1962.

CHAPTER ELEVEN

PSYCHOTHERAPY AND ITS CRITICS

1. Culture and Neurosis

IT was stated in Chapter 1 that it would need a cultural revolution to facilitate the solution of the problem of mental illness on a large scale. Our existing culture is, in many respects, violently opposed to the true spirit of psychotherapy. Even its democracies have developed new authoritarianisms, and our modern world favours the critic of psychotherapy rather than the therapist. The perpetuation of the struggles for political power, and the easy assumption that the improvement of the material standard of living is the main thing to aim at, and will put everything right, creates an atmosphere in which patient understanding of the mentally ill is most likely to give way to impatient resentment. It is a culture of power-worship, of the scientific manipulation of every aspect of existence, of the power of 'mind over matter' and of 'mind over mind'. One of the best antidotes to facile optimism about the solution of the mental health problem, is to keep on reminding ourselves of the subtle, far-reaching and often overpowering effects of our cultural environment on the states of mind of the individual, so often for ill and not for good.

Our culture praises ambition, striving, the competitive spirit, to keep everyone at full stretch, and the achievement of the kinds of success which rest on someone else's failure or defeat. This power cult is regarded as virile and vital. I am not decrying competition altogether, particularly as a stimulus to pleasurable effort in leisure time activities. But as a philosophy of life it is rooted in insecurity and fear of failure, it implies that every other person is a potential enemy, and glorifies truculent self-assertion and 'toughness' rather than the capacity to co-operate for the common good, in individuals, classes and nations. It overlooks the difference between a spontaneous flow of energy in a healthy and non-anxious mind and a forced self-driving in the face of energy-sapping insecurity. Political neuroses on a national and international scale and the neuroses of ill and suffering individuals are but the opposite poles of the same basic problem, the ramifications of fear in human life.

In saying that a cultural revolution is necessary, I am not

calling simply for new ideas. History is strewn with examples of new ideologies, purporting to aim at producing a heaven on earth for common humanity; whether they be religious ideologies aiming at the conversion of multitudes, or political ideologies proceeding by way of social and economic revolution, they all arrive at the point where the leaders fall victim to a lust for power, and the new movement ceases to provide peace and security for the mass of human beings and becomes a power-cult aiming at the elimination of rival ideologies. No doubt political security from the dangers of war and economic distress are necessary to rule out our primary material fears for our physical existence. In times of gross material insecurity and danger human beings are not likely to become particularly mentally healthy. But peace and prosperity are by no means an infallible recipe for mental health. The increase of leisure and the multiplication of means and opportunities for its use, along with the increasing demand for the luxuries of life, is visibly leading to a mental outlook on parenthood and family life which is calculated to bring up anything but secure children. Young parents find so many allurements outside the home and feel so much 'out of fashion' if they do not avail themselves of them by means of paid 'baby-sitters' (suitable or otherwise) that it easy to say, 'Oh! the baby's all right, he'll be asleep'. In spite of the diffusion of psychological knowledge today, it is very likely that the mothers of less sophisticated times gave more of their simple affectionate humanity to their children than many young mothers of today do. It is of little use criticizing 'the present generation' for every generation is largely the product of its times. Whether in insecurity or in prosperity, modern civilization is very far from fostering mental health. If this were not so, we would not be having to consider what Eysenck called the 'frightening incidence' (cp. p. 22) of mental disorders in modern life. The cultural revolution we need is one that fundamentally revises our scale of values concerning security.

On this question I would like to quote some words from an after-dinner speech given at the London School of Economics by my daughter, Mrs. D. Greenald, M.A. After mentioning the 'atmosphere of equality within the community' at L.S.E. and the complete acceptance of 'every nationality, race, class, creed, political opinion, personal idiosyncracy, and sex equality,' she added:

> 'Equality of the sexes is, so far, equality in a man's world. This was a necessary beginning, but we are still a long way from equality of status between the sexes. Society places a far higher

value on careers outside the family than on the vocation of bringing up children. Only when the rewards for both become comparable will full equality of status be attained. . . . If Mrs. Beatrice Webb (founder of L.S.E.) were alive today, I feel sure she would be devoting her vast energy to a study of the missing element in the social reforms of the past half century. And I venture to suggest that this missing element is the further reform of the most basic of our institutions—the family—and, in particular, the role of the mother within it. Today we know the family to be the key member of our institutions, and it is widely accepted that much of our society's sickness, in particular crime and neurosis, is directly traceable to something going wrong within the family. Since prevention is the only long-term answer, I feel that the outstanding need of today is for parents to learn how to bring up their children in wisdom and love, and to feel that this is a job of supreme social value. Our present educational system evades this issue from the primary school upwards, and concentrates its efforts on preparing the young for a career outside the family. Women graduates are well fitted to compete in a man's world, but on the whole very ill-fitted to switch roles after a few years and become responsible for rearing tomorrow's citizens. The School (L.S.E.) does, in fact, provide a considerable body of teaching, particularly in its Social Science Faculty, which contributes to this end, but the fact that it does so is incidental. Its organization and purpose is for the training of social workers and social administrators, not future parents. Bringing up children has lightly been regarded by our society as something which anybody can do, without special training. Yet surely unless society can begin to use the body of knowledge which has now been accumulated, it will not get the type of citizens it needs.'

It is certainly true that no one would dream of putting a person in charge of a complex and costly piece of machinery with as little training and knowledge about it as most young parents have about babies. It is useless and wrong in principle to blame parents, for they are themselves the products of the social and personal tensions they perpetuate; and in dealing with their children, only reflect the damage done to them. This is not a particularly easy problem to overcome, but the way needs to be found. If this point of view is taken together with the way in which the international struggle for power holds a sword of Damocles over the heads of humanity in the mass in the atom age, we must conclude that it is above all important to avoid superficial diagnoses, and over-optimistic expectations of this or that kind of treatment. The longer we remain blind to the facts, the longer we expose ourselves and others to suffering. I would be prepared to say that in the long run the greatest contribution made by psychotherapeutic research is not to the 'curing' of individuals but to the accumulation of the kind of knowledge which will help on the cause of prevention.

Nevertheless, suffering individuals have the right to seek and demand help for themselves as well as for future generations, and in furthering our study of what psychotherapy can offer, we can only answer that question if we understand the kind of difficulties psychotherapy has to contend with. The individual we seek to 'cure' is not an isolated being but a small unit in a vast whole, the product of an ever increasingly complex society and world, in which it is clearly very difficult for children to grow up non-anxious, fear-free and mentally healthy. If it were not so, mental illness would not be so widespread. We can take Professor Eysenck's statistics (cp. p. 23) further. We know too much now to deceive ourselves with the view that the problem is contained within the limits of psychosis (insanity) as a fixed 3 per cent of the population and psychoneurosis as around 50 per cent of the G.P.'s patients. The dimensions of the problem are far greater than that. Mental illness ramifies all the way down from psychosis and specific 'nervous' illness, through crime and delinquency and pathological personalities who are a menace to the community in public, political and economic life, to chronic discontent, tension and inability to relax, insomnia, quarrelsomeness and coldness amongst people in general, with inability to maintain stable and friendly personal relationships in work and home life. Mental ill-health is ultimately not the fault of the individual, but something forced on him by the failure of the world into which he has been born as a helpless infant, at the mercy of whatever treatment awaits him. Thus Dr. D. Winnicott described schizophrenia as 'an environmental deficiency disease'.*

What concerns the psychotherapist is that *the cultural set-up in which neurosis and distortion of personality are developed, is the worst possible one in which to try to cure it.* Relatives of patients frequently show little understanding of what is the real trouble or of what the therapist is seeking to do. They usually seem to expect the therapist to produce a quick and magical 'cure' which will make the patient easier for them to get on with. Often the security one slowly builds up in the consulting room is broken down by uncomprehending people who deal with the patient in his

* *Collected Papers,* p. 162.

everyday life. Many influences conspire to make the patient who is seeking psychotherapeutic help feel guilty about doing so, and hypersensitive about anyone knowing of it.

It is true that, once deeply disturbed in childhood and then left without adequate help in growing up emotionally, human beings struggle gallantly to make something of their lives. I have often wondered how some patients were able to stick it so long, and have felt genuine admiration for the way they have wrestled blindly for years with disabilities they did not understand. In such conditions whatever is gained is only achieved by a process of self-driving, the price of which is self-exhaustion and probably psychosomatic illness at last. But in idealizing this as a positive virtue of self-discipline and self-denial, our culture glorifies something which is the product of the condition we want to cure. Religion has often been led astray into presenting virtue as synonymous with treating oneself harshly, overlooking the fact that those who treat themselves harshly are nearly always driven to treat others in the same way. A vicious circle is created. A neurotic culture breeds neurotic individuals who in turn maintain the neurotic culture to put strains on their children. This aspect of the problem has, for the first time, been brought out clearly in our lifetime by the investigations of sociologists and anthropologists. It is a point of view we should never lose, for it is an effective safeguard against easy optimism about the treatment of mental illness. It explains the atmosphere of misunderstanding and prejudice in which psychotherapy so often has to work, and which is one major difficulty it has to encounter.

Mental illness in the last resort has its roots in the total set-up of the world's life today, and more immediately in the family set-up within that world. In the end, that is the real reason why psycho-analytic therapy, the one treatment which aims at a radical 'cure', proves in practice to be so lengthy and difficult a process, and to be beset by so many limitations and discouragements. One might think that it is attempting to do the impossible, though having been engaged in this form of therapy for a quarter of a century I am satisfied that genuine good results can be and are produced.

2. 'Behaviour Therapy'

Before we examine more closely the nature and problems of radical psychotherapy, it will be wise first to see what its critics have to say. My main reason for doing this here is that, in relation to the point of view I have just outlined, the critics mostly seem to be people who want to reduce the problem of mental illness to a false simplification. On this basis, they can exhibit their impatience with psychoanalytic therapy for not producing more striking and speedy results. By contrast the psychotherapist has learned to be suspicious of striking and speedy results which so often do not last, and he is content to go along with his patients while they 'grow' at whatever rate is possible for them. I have never observed that human beings are very amenable to being forced, even when it is supposed to be for their own good. One of my patients recently said to me: 'I have just been reading that a London psychiatrist says that the "talking cure" is out and the "drug cure" is in.' This patient, however, preferred to go on with the 'talking cure' since she had tried the 'drug cure' first and found that it did not 'cure'; it had helped her to some extent to control and carry on but had left all her personality problems as serious and puzzling as ever.

As an example of hostile criticism of psychoanalysis and psycho-therapy I shall take the views of Professor Eysenck, partly because there was a lively debate about them in the *Guardian* (April and May, 1961), which aroused much public interest, and partly because he has achieved a mild notoriety for his anti-psychotherapy propaganda, in favour of what he terms 'behaviour therapy'. This appears to me to be a striking example of the over-simplification of the problem to which I have referred. It is not my purpose to examine closely the behaviour therapy Eysenck advocates. That would be more in place in a purely technical book, and I am primarily concerned with his attack on psycho-therapy because it is in many ways typical of the critics of this method. But in his article in the *Guardian*, he gave an account of behaviour therapy which involves not only an over-simplified but even superficial account of neurosis. He suggested that there is no underlying cause of a neurotic symptom, no 'unconscious motivation' in the Freudian sense, but that the symptom is itself the illness, is nothing more than an emotional and behavioural habit, a 'conditioned response' or 'reflex' which was psycho-physically acquired in early life and is capable of being extin-guished by reconditioning techniques proved in the laboratory. Such a view seems to be strangely out of touch with the stories of stark tragedy, hate and unhappiness one hears in the consult-ing room. I am reminded of one patient who was sent for psycho-analytic treatment in a seriously ill condition and apparently on the verge of life-long invalidism. After four years of analysis every physical symptom had gone. That was ten years ago and I am in a position to know that this patient's physical health has remained excellent to this day. But at that time she said: 'Physically I'm cured, I've never been so well for years, but I've never been so unhappy. I know now how full of hate our family life is.' It was at this point that the treatment, not of symptoms but of the real trouble began. The hysteric so regularly converts personal and human problems into physical symptoms that it is astonishing that Eysenck should assert that there is nothing behind the symptoms and that they are the illness. In one session this patient was talking of the violent quarrels between her parents when she was a child, and developed a sudden attack of migraine. Gripping her head she literally cried out, 'They're all quarrelling in my head now and I can't stand it'. This migraine which had plagued her for years was one of the symptoms which has been completely removed.

The *Guardian* correspondence arose out of a review of Eysenck's chapter on 'The Effects of Psychotherapy' in the *Handbook of Abnormal Psychology*.* In the same book Dr. H. Gwynne Jones gives a careful and less provocative account of behaviour therapy than that of Eysenck, in the chapter on 'Applied Abnormal Psychology'. His view, however, is essentially the same in principle. He writes: 'In terms of this type of theory (i.e. theories of learning) neuroses are behavioural abnormalities which include ideational response components but do not derive from some psychic entity lying behind the symptomatic manifestations. If this analysis is valid all treatment must be symptomatic: if all symptoms are removed so is the neurosis.'† There is no reason to deny that there can be such things as superficial 'bad behavioural habits' which could be eliminated by the behaviour therapist's laboratory techniques of 'reconditioning', and that would obviously have its uses. There is such a thing as 'conditioning' or 'emotional scarring' creating habits which outlive their usefulness. A reconditioning technique may rid the patient of the habit which he cannot voluntarily eliminate. This has not yet been properly married to psychotherapy, and emotional injury at a very vulnerable period may leave an indelible mark. But as a definition of neurosis this is simply grossly inadequate. *The major problem of neurosis is not this or that symptom but the fundamentally fear-ridden and inwardly weakened, emotionally undermined, and developmentally arrested state of the patient as a total self.* This, of course, differs in degree from one patient to another, but this is the real problem. Dr. Jones writes of the treatment of symptoms such as stammering, hysterical glove anaesthesia, writer's cramp etc. Every analyst will have seen such

* London, Pitman, 1960.
† Ibid. p. 774.

symptoms disappear in the course of analysis, sometimes to return again at times of especial stress for the patient. I once had a patient with an hysterical tremor of one limb and 'nothing else to worry about'. However, about once a year he did have a vague week-end depression. As analysis proceeded the depressions got more frequent and the tremor improved, and his dreams began to reveal that he secretly felt helpless and paralysed as a total self. This feeling had, so to speak, been shut up in the trembling limb. The investigation of symptom-plus-self showed him that this feeling of paralysed helplessness characterized not so much his limb as his personality. He dreamed that he went down into the basement and found there a young man just like himself held in the grip of an octopus. He began to hack at the tentacles to set him free, and then suddenly threw down his knife, went out and locked the door, and went back upstairs turning his back on the whole thing. One is reminded of the play entitled *Dear Octopus*, where the octopus is the mother of a large family from whose tentacles none of the members can escape. By what right does the behaviour therapist choose to set aside such evidence of the patient's own inner life, and decide that there is nothing behind the symptom.

Dr. Gwynne Jones writes: 'As to techniques of treatment . . . modification of behaviour is the aim.'* In that case the issue between behaviour therapy and psychotherapy is this: (a) for the behaviour therapist, personality is a set of behavioural habits with no significant self behind them. (b) for the psychotherapist, personality is the social functioning of a total psychic self, a significant person, whose behaviour expresses in a meaningful way the state he is in, whether it be normal or abnormal. The psychotherapist is not concerned with the symptoms as such, but with helping a whole but undermined and weakened person who is struggling along feeling not able to stand up to life adequately. The 'monosymtomatic neurosis', of which the above example is an illustration, must be a headache to the behaviour therapist, for the removal of the single symptom so frequently discloses the most far-reaching disturbance of the personality as a whole.

Eysenck puts his point of view uncompromisingly and it is difficult to find in his theory anything more than another version of old-fashioned materialistic or mechanistic views of human nature, in which the physical organism is the reality and the 'person', as a 'whole being' for whom life has a meaning, can be ignored. For him a neurosis with a variety of symptoms is a collection of

* Ibid. pp. 774-5.

separate fixed 'habits' which can be stamped out one by one piece-meal. The illness is not treated as a meaningful whole expressing the total disturbed relationship of a 'person' with his environ-ment. He reduces psychology to an impersonal science, a phy-siological psychology of conditioned responses and reflexes which, he says, is based on the work of Pavlov (1890) and J. B. Watson (1910). 'Curing neuroses' he regards as 'identical with the methods used for extinguishing conditioned reflexes.'* This reduces not only the human being with a neurosis but all human beings to the level of a psychophysical automaton. When he attacks psycho-therapy he is comparing a method of suppressing symptoms as separate bits and pieces of past psychophysical 'conditioning', with a method which aims at the far more difficult and compre-hensive task of releasing a whole person, who is fundamentally crippled by fear, for full and mature development. There is no real comparison. His view suggests a picture of a human being as a ball with a number of nasty labels stuck on. These can be rubbed off and nice labels stuck in their place. But the ball itself remains unchanged. Such a 'model' bears no relation to the reality of personality.

Thus bed-wetting is treated as nothing but a meaningless habit based on failure to learn control. So it is arranged that an electrical device shall ring a bell and wake the child the moment it begins to wet the bed, and conscious control is established. That seems to be conclusive. Patients have described to me how as children they would lie awake at night controlling their bladder, in fear that once they fell asleep they would wet the bed. Of course, if they could be wakened in the act, conscious control would be once more re-established. But why do they wet the bed when asleep? This may be just faulty formation of the habit of control, but what if in other cases it has a deeper meaning and is a tension-relieving sympton which is really calling attention to an emotional problem the child cannot solve without help? Every psychotherapist has observed that many of his patients in their anxious phases are for ever wanting to 'spend a penny' even while they are wide awake. They do not lack control, and it is not the urination but the anxiety-tension behind it that calls for cure. Eysenck, however, says that there is nothing behind the symp-tom. How then would he explain this case? The mother of a little girl was an extremely aloof, cold, unfeeling person (what is termed 'schizoid') and her child was a chronic bed-wetter. In the course of psychoanalytical treatment of the mother, her per-sonality began to open out and her husband said, 'You don't

* The *Guardian*.

freeze me off so much now'. At this stage she reported that her
child had suddenly stopped bed-wetting. Some months later an
objectively anxious situation in real life frightened her and sent
her into her shell again markedly, and she reported that her child
had started bed-wetting once more. What is the use of forcibly
stopping the bed-wetting while the child feels unloved by her
mother, and how can it be held that the sympton is the illness?
The illness is the child's chronic separation-anxiety and feeling
of utter insecurity and weakness as a small person. If behaviour
therapy could find a way of 'reconditioning' the mother so as to
turn an unhappy schizoid woman into a warm-hearted and loving
individual, that really would be something. But there is no sign of
that being possible except as a response to a good, healing,
human relationship and this psychotherapy seeks to provide.

In the *Guardian* Dr. Gwynne Jones gave a more reasonable
account of behaviour therapy than that of Eysenck, and if any
bit of 'reconditioning technique' developed by this school proves
useful in suppressing symptoms, I would welcome it in the same
way, and with the same reservations, as I do the existing psychiatric techniques (drugs, E.C.T., etc.) for doing the same job. But
in neither case should we regard the result in any meaningful
sense as a radical cure of mental ill-health. Dr. Gwynne Jones
obviously repudiated Eysenck's exaggerated enthusiasm for behaviour therapy, and from within the behaviour therapist's own
camp, when he wrote, 'Whatever the therapeutic shortcomings of
psychoanalysis and other forms of psychotherapy, behaviour
therapy is certainly not a proven alternative and is probably not
even developed to a stage at which it could be routinely applied.'
What is important in Eysenck's view of behaviour therapy is not
its technique, but the philosophy of man on which it rests. By all
means let research into this and every other form of therapy,
partial or radical, go on. Any help that can be given in coping
with symptons, if with nothing else, will have its uses provided its
limitations are recognized.

Meanwhile we must turn to the wholly negative view Eysenck
presents of psychotherapy, for this raises far more important
matters than the *ad hoc* suppression of symptoms. I am not at
all concerned to deny or hide the therapeutic shortcomings of
psychoanalysis and psychotherapy. On the contrary it is important to make them as clear and unambiguous as is possible, so
that we may investigate the limitations and find out what exactly
they are, why they exist, how they may be overcome, and what
light they throw on the immense problem of restoring a human
being to mental health. There is a useful level of pure symptom

therapy. Symptoms can and do over-develop and get out of hand, but it is quite possible to reduce and eliminate them, as behaviour therapy seeks to do, without curing the real trouble. We saw in the last chapter, that simple psychoanalytical explanation can sometimes banish symptoms, without any 'reconditioning technique'. But such symptom-treatment plainly left deeper troubles unresolved.

I find no difficulty at all in accepting Dr. Gwynne Jones's modest and honest claim for behaviour therapy. He writes: 'It needs to be stated that, though the apparently successful treatment of a few cases has been described, other cases, treated on similar lines have not been successful. It is not claimed that the remainder necessarily improved as a result of the treatment received, nor that behavioural retraining techniques are superior to psychotherapeutic procedures. What is claimed is the possibility of devising treatments derived from the findings of experimental psychology.'* Eysenck, however, is not so modest and does definitely claim not only the superiority of behaviour therapy but the uselessness of psychotherapy.

In his account of neurosis, in fact, he shifts his ground. In 1953, in *The Uses and Abuses of Psychology*, he put the main emphasis on the view that the ultimate cause of neurosis is an innate, *constitutional neuroticism* which is incurable, a predisposition to react with anxiety and fear to everything, about which we can do nothing. He wrote:

'There is good evidence to suggest that neurotic reactions appear largely on an inherited basis and that a person's liability to break down under stress is a property of his nervous system, which is unlikely to be affected to any considerable extent by psychotherapy.'†

This argument is curious. There is no general agreement that this statement is true. There are undoubtedly inherited differences in human beings and those which are important for neurosis are of the order of 'innate sensitivity' which varies in subtle ways from one person to another. Eysenck's label for this, innate *neuroticism*, is highly questionable. Dr. J. D. Sutherland (Medical Director, Tavistock Clinic) suggested (in a private communication) that one could carry out tests of Eysenck's type in any medical outpatient department and quite easily isolate a factor of 'ill healthicism' which shows the lack of meaning in Eysenck's 'neu-

* *Abnormal Psych.*, p. 778.
† Pelican Books, p. 206.

roticism', except as a term of denigration. But that is not the point here. The real point is that he is using this argument to create a prejudice against the value of psychotherapy. In fact, if this view were true, then behaviour therapy and all other forms of therapy would be equally useless. Moreover the theory of the behaviour therapist is explicitly that there is no neurosis other than the symptoms and that there is nothing behind the symptoms, but now Eysenck tells us that the real trouble is evidently not the symptoms at all, but innate 'neuroticism' which must lie behind the symptoms as the real cause of trouble.

On the other hand, to create a basis for behaviour therapy, Eysenck has to proceed by drawing a distinction between his 'innate neuroticism' and 'neurosis'. He says:

'One must carefully distinguish between *neuroticism*, i.e. the inherited emotional instability which predisposes a person to form neurotic symptoms under stress, and ultimately have a nervous breakdown, and *neurosis*, the result of the imposition of emotional stress on a nervous system predisposed to react through the neurotic mechanisms.'*

So that, after all we are still dealing with the pressures of the environment on the child. I certainly know of cases of parental mishandling of children which would have distorted a cast-iron constitution: while it is equally true that there are many highly sensitive people who do not suffer from neurosis, having been fortunate in a very secure childhood. In dealing with mental ill-health, we are not dealing with just the liability to produce certain types of symptom which Eysenck calls the 'neurotic mechanisms', but with the distortion of the whole personality into hate, guilt, an incapacity to love in spite of an intense need for love, and deepest of all fear that undermines and weakens the whole self. If innate neuroticism does not rule out behaviour therapy, neither does it *a priori* rule out psychotherapy, and his earlier argument falls to the ground as an attempt to prejudice the issue. Once we admit that the results of early experience are treatable, the *personal* 'reconditioning' by means of a good psychotherapeutic relationship has as good a right to recognition as the *impersonal* techniques of behaviour therapy.

3. *The Nature of Psychotherapy*
We have now raised the question of the nature of psychotherapy

* Ibid. pp. 207-8.

itself, and this bears tremendously on Eysenck's views. I do not accept his definition of psychotherapy at all. He writes:

'Psychotherapy may be defined as a systematic and persistent exploration of a neurotic patient's mental processes by verbal means in order to help him towards better personal and social integration.'*

This definition is a survival from the early days of Freudian theory, when Freud himself, like Eysenck, was dominated by the ideal of a purely and narrowly scientific psychotherapy. Perhaps the idea has never quite died out in psychoanalysis that the 'investigation' is the curative agency. This is often expressed in the notion that 'insight' cures. In fact, it would be more true to say that insight develops as the healing of deep fear proceeds, and marked insight registers the end of one phase of progress and opens the way to the next. Freud himself early stressed the fact that to give purely intellectual insight or explanation only results in two versions of the neurosis existing in the mind at the same time, an intellectual one in consciousness and the original and real one, the emotional neurosis, in the unconscious.

Another discovery of Freud bears greatly on this question, namely, what he called 'transference'. The fact emerged that whatever the therapist's view of the relationship was, the patient did not regard it as a purely scientific one. He reacted emotionally, and when he felt in a good relationship with his therapist his symptoms receded, and when he felt in a bad relationship his symptoms would rush back again. This, incidentally, disproves the view that there is nothing behind the symptoms. The meaning of this fact was somewhat obscured by Freud's view that attachments were always basically sexual, and he regarded this phenomenon as the 'transference' to the analyst of the patient's childhood sexual love and hate for parents. We have seen how, in the course of time, emphasis on sex came to be replaced by emphasis on aggression in psychoanalytic theory, and I believe it is in process of being displaced once more to a still more fundamental emphasis on fear. What the child and every human being needs first and foremost is *security as a personality*. The satisfaction of instinctive needs is only a part of this overall problem. The infant depends on his mother primarily for his security, not just as a body but as a whole if immature human being, for the safety of his existence as an individual and growing person. It is this need which the patient transfers to the therapist, and not a

* Op. cit. p. 195.

narrowly sexual drive. What the patient above all must have is the
kind of relationship with the therapist which will enable him to
come by a feeling of basic security in his personality, which his
parents were unable to give him in sufficient measure in infancy
and childhood.

I would not expect psychotherapy as Eysenck defines it, namely
as 'systematic and persistent exploration of a neurotic's mental
processes by verbal means' to produce a 'cure'. If, in the therapeutic failures Eysenck gives statistics about, this is all that psychotherapy amounted to, then I think failure or very limited success
could have been predicted beforehand. It is my own conclusion, on surveying the results of some quarter of a century of my
own practice, that the patients who arrived at the best results
were those who succeeded in feeling the most genuine trust in me
as therapist; not a blind trust in what I said or in my opinions,
but a trust with insight into the genuineness of my care, concern,
and respect for them, and my reliability as a person. I find that
these characteristics are even more important than 'understanding'. No therapist can always understand everything about his
patient at once, but if the patient trusts him as a person, that
patient knows that the two of them will be able to work together
and arrive at understanding sooner or later. Meanwhile the patient
is slowly feeling more and more real as a person in himself. But
the more ill a patient is, the more unable he is even to tolerate
such an investigation. It is a sign that he is feeling safer with the
therapist when he can do so. The 'cure' must have already begun
before the 'investigation' can get under way to any considerable
extent. The position taken today is rather that the 'investigation'
is a method of finding out what is wrong, so that the curative
factor, a security-giving relationship with the therapist, can be
brought to bear on it.

One of the things that for long hindered the therapeutic
effectiveness of psychoanalysis and caused recurrent waves of
pessimism to afflict analysts, was the view that treatment should be
kept strictly 'scientific', and that insight given by impersonal
investigation would promote a cure. This impersonality is becoming a thing of the past, one reason being that the more ill
and distressed the patient is, the more impossible it is to be
scientifically impersonal with him. The patient cannot tolerate it
and will not let the analyst be impersonal. Years ago I began by
adopting the usual analytic practice of asking the patient to lie on
a couch and talk away. The more ill the patient was, the more I
found that one of two things would happen. Either the patient
would lie on the couch in a completely shut in and detached state

of mind, and talk away from a purely superficial intellectual level, indulging in what Eysenck calls: 'systematic and persistent exploration of mental processes by verbal means', feeling nothing and getting nowhere, as with a very schizoid man who said, 'If I didn't lie here where I can't see you, I wouldn't be able to talk at all': or else, if the patient's emotional distress was conscious, he could not stand the isolation, was restless and fidgety on the couch, would twist around so that he could see the therapist, and most likely in the end just get up and say, 'I can't stand it here, I must sit nearer to you', and pull a chair up. Patients should be allowed to sit wherever they feel most at ease. One highly important problem is that the patient often discovers that he feels just as frightened at being too near the therapist as too far away, and will choose a half-way position, even sitting on the floor or on a stool in front of the fire, close enough to feel reassured and supported and far enough away to feel he is preserving independence. This can be most valuable in helping him to bring out with the therapist his basic conflicts between his *needs* and *fears* of real human relationship. Thus the 'investigation' which slowly brings to light the frightened child out of the depths of the unconscious, is only likely to get far if it goes along with a supportive relationship which enables the child inside the ill adult to feel secure. The highly controlled intellectual patient who can never allow treatment to be any more than a calm scientific investigation, and who feels that it is humiliating to need help at all, may gain a lot of intellectual understanding and learn a lot of psychology, but at the end of the process he is practically unchanged.

These facts show up the limitations of Eysenck's behaviour therapy. This rests on an attempt to be purely scientific by working out 'techniques' for reconditioning the patient. The 'scientist' in this case is spared the arduous task of achieving, and helping the patient to achieve, a reliable human relationship which will give him a chance to regrow his personality. A purely impersonal technique is operated. This is far easier for the person doing the treating, but the patient is robbed of the only thing that can be of final value to him. We might use Eysenck's terminology and say that, once the deepest and most disturbed part of the patient's personality is brought to light, a reliable, understanding good relationship with the therapist can 'recondition' the patient to a more secure feeling about himself and about life. But this *personal* type of 'reconditioning' is very different from, and far more natural than, the impersonal laboratory-tested techniques which aim at stamping out habits. It would be possible to stamp out the nocturnal enuresis of the child unloved by her mother but that is not going to make her feel a secure and non-anxious child.

I cannot, therefore, accept Eysenck's definition of psycho-therapy, and would say that *psychotherapy is a personal security-giving relationship which offers the patient a chance to outgrow fear, and in which therefore a method of investigation can be used to bring the relationship to bear at the important points where the patient experiences conflict, tension and anxiety.* To give a relatively simple example, a young man whose personality and speech were inhibited and his self-confidence destroyed by a sarcastic father, finds himself slowly talking more freely and opening out to express himself and his own ideas because he finds himself listened to with respect and not ridiculed. Eysenck favours methods that do not rely on the co-operation of the person *qua* person, but seek to force something on him. In psychotherapy such procedures would be ruled out. The psychoanalyst is not determined to make the patient give up the symptom at all cost. Often its continuance is an incentive to seek a needed personality-change, and when that is secured the symptom will fade out of itself. There is, in fact, a dangerous implication in treating human beings as anything less than persons. Eysenck wants to 'do something' to people to compel them to give up their symptoms. It is a 'power-technique', and it fully justifies the comment of a patient who had read the *Guardian* correspondence: 'I wouldn't let Eysenck work on me with his reconditioning. I'll talk to you because you listen and help me to understand.' I have just received a notice of a book entitled *The Manipulation of Human Behaviour* (Wiley Bookservice) which states: 'In recent years concern has been ex-pressed in both popular and scholarly literature regarding the dangers posed by scientific developments which could be used to control and manipulate human behaviour.' This concern is fully justified and I fear Behaviour Therapy must come under it, for it is an impersonal technique. The essence of psychotherapy is an atmosphere of complete freedom from any pressure on or manipulation of the patient. An editorial comment on this matter appeared in the *Nursing Times* (April 5, 1963). 'Certain methods of treatment which are being employed in some psychiatric hos-pitals are giving rise to disquiet among nurses. . . . These are methods based on Pavlovian conditioning theory, designed to break down undesirable patterns of behaviour. . . . Aversion therapy for the treatment of alcoholism has been in use for a number of years. . . . Now similar techniques—sometimes using apomorphine and sometimes other unpleasant stimuli such as electric shocks —are being used in a wide variety of behaviour disorders. Par-ticularly notable is their use in certain forms of sexual deviation.

. . . In some ways behaviour therapy resembles the technique which in the hands of political and military authorities is known as "brain washing". In the course of treatment intended to change the patient's attitudes of mind as well as his patterns of behaviour, his physical and his mental resistance may be lowered and he may be subjected to great physical discomfort and even pain. The use of these methods obviously calls for a convincing ethical justification. In the first place, is it right that they should be used at all?; secondly, is there not a danger that such methods might increasingly be used to bolster a conformist society rather than because the individual is truly sick and needs treatment? . . . Although, in theory, these patients submit to this treatment voluntarily, some of them are in hospital because a court has placed them on probation on condition that they should enter hospital for treatment.'

When a patient says simply: 'I was brought up in fear and not in love', the psychotherapist has to create an atmosphere in which a basically crushed person can regain confidence in human relationship and begin to regrow a true self. That is something that cannot be done by drugs, by any form of physical treatment, by any reconditioning techniques, or by any technique at all. It can only be done by the therapist being the kind of person in whom the patient can come to feel confidence at last; but this is the really fundamental thing that psychotherapy aims to do. The 'techniques' of various kinds are valuable to relieve burdensome symptoms, reduce tensions and prop the patient against the stress of his anxiety, and under favourable conditions may even succeed in rehabilitating some patients socially and domestically. That must not be confused with radical cure, and long-term psychotherapy seeks to do the absolutely radical job of helping a human being to regrow out of fear. Just because it attempts so much, its difficulties and chances of failure are correspondingly high. *It is far easier to criticize psychotherapy than to do it,* but if we are going to take human beings seriously as persons, the attempt must be made.

Eysenck's 'reconditioning techniques' could be very useful to political dictators who want to turn us all into party stereotypes, but they do not look to be capable of creating mature and loving human beings. This can only be done by a fundamental regrowth out of fear. What Eysenck calls 'innate neuroticism' is more truly seen as the deep bottom layer of fear, developed in the earliest years, which underlies the later developed neurosis and its symptoms, and finds expression in them. We do not need to fall back on the idea of inherited neuroticism. There is no human infant, of whatever hereditary toughness of constitution, who cannot be made afraid, and if too much fear is aroused in him too early, his struggles to master it will distort his personality and drive him into some form of either illness or antisocial human relationships. Psychotherapy sets itself the ambitious task of getting to the personal roots of the trouble.

Curiously enough, Eysenck makes an admission which unwittingly concedes this very point. He writes:

'The most useful part for psychotherapy to play may be not as a *substitute* for these more fundamental methods but rather as an *adjunct*. Some of the writers who have used habit-breaking methods of the type described here have added a statement to the effect that in their view, psychotherapy should accompany the treatment. That seems a reasonable point of view; there are stresses and strains arising in the breaking of any firmly anchored habit which may require the help of an outsider, as they would otherwise be beyond the patient's ability to bear without impairing his nervous stability.'*

After all then it is not the 'habits' but the underlying anxiety against which they were a defence which is the real trouble. This breaks loose as soon as the defence is removed. At that point Eysenck concedes that a human relationship is needed to enable the sufferer to withstand his own inner insecurity. I would wish for no better recognition of the role of psychotherapy, but I would exactly reverse Eysenck's statement of its relationship to symptom-suppressing methods, and say that symptom-suppressing methods are an adjunct to and not a substitute for psychotherapy. A combination of psychotherapy and electro-convulsive therapy, for example, is often used when possible. Psychotherapy plods away at the basic work of personality-reconstruction as a slow regrowing process in a good security-giving relationship, while E.C.T. is called in if necessary to take care of acute phases of emotional disturbance during which psychotherapy may become impossible and the patient may need protection from the intensity of his own tensions.

4. The Critic of Psychotherapy

Since the above admission, however, is really an inconsistency, we find that since 1953 Eysenck has moved more and more to the position of seeking to decry and disprove psychotherapy alto-

* *The Uses and Abuses of Psychology,* pp. 219-20.

gether. He has rushed to the attack in popular articles in *The Readers Digest* (Feb. 1960) and in *Discovery* (April 1961), and on a more technical level in *The Handbook of Abnormal Psychology* already quoted. It was a review of this contribution by Wayland Young in the *Guardian* that started the correspondence referred to. Young, who described Eysenck as 'one of the heavy-weights of our time in destructive polemics', says that, 'In 1952 he advanced the hypothesis that psychotherapy in the usually accepted sense did no good at all, and claimed that this could not be disproved. . . . He now goes further and very nearly claims that the hypothesis is proven.' Young writes certainly not as a scientist but as an enthusiast for 'Eysenck Iconoclastes' and says that, 'His survey of the literature is a real knock-out blow.' As to that we shall see. One of the unvarying features of the history of psycho-analysis, from the earliest days of Freud, has been the emotional hostility displayed by its critics. They never seem able to attempt even a scientific assessment without ending up with emotionally toned derogatory remarks aimed at creating a prejudice against it. Dogmatic assertions, having all the appearance of being factual, abound in such attacks, and Eysenck himself is conspicuous for such tactics.

We need not ask why Eysenck, on the subject of psychotherapy, is not a scientist but a controversialist and propagandist, but the fact has to be noted. There is no evidence in his writings of his having any first-hand knowledge of psychotherapy and its diffi-culties. In his contribution to the *Guardian* he wrote that psycho-analysis is 'brain-washing', 'magic', 'dogma', 'temperamental pref-erence rather than science', and that 'Freud is the darling of the rhubarb intelligentsia'. To the serious enquirer, this is not scien-tific writing but highly emotional propaganda. He wants to dis-credit psychoanalysis. The scientific temper of mind does not waste time trying to pull down other people's houses but seeks patiently to build its own. If he were content simply to devote his time to discovering the best that can be done in developing techniques for suppressing symptoms, he would no doubt dis-cover something of practical value in giving quick relief from disabling symptoms so that patients could then feel less stress in facing life and be able to consider whether they wanted to go into the deeper causes. Not every case would be helpfully treated this way, but there are cases where initial symptom relief is im-portant and necessary. Everything he discovered would be wel-comed by all of us, though we would want to know all about its after-effects. For the problem of treating mental ill-health is so vast that we cannot afford to ignore anything that has any value in relieving human suffering, whether the relief be temporary or far-reaching.

But Eysenck is not content with that. He must be attacking other people's lines of approach and naïvely assumes that only he is scientific. The reviewer of his book *The Uses and Abuses of Psychology*, in *The Times Literary Supplement*, however, rejected his claim to be so purely scientific. His method is to make dogmatic statements and to keep on repeating them. Thus he writes:

> 'Some psychologists who ought to know better are firmly convinced (on emotional grounds) of the truth of the Freudian dogma . . . long after his system had become nothing but a sooterkin to scientific investigators.'*

In the magazine *Discovery* he wrote:

> 'The fact that there is no scientifically acceptable, positive evidence for the therapeutic value of psychoanalysis is now so widely accepted among experts that I shall not waste space in order to document this point any further; it is largely among laymen (teachers, social workers, and others with only a vague smattering of psychology) that a belief in the efficacy of psychotherapy and the unique benefits of psychoanalysis is still found.'

I do not know whether teachers, social workers etc., who usually in practice have a good deal of understanding of human nature and are not particularly credulous, will appreciate being relegated by Eysenck in this superior way to his class of 'rhubarb intelligentsia', but we must ask who are these 'experts' and 'scientific investigators'. Eysenck must be choosing to remember only those who happen to agree with him, for in fact, the number of psychiatrists and psychologists seeking psychoanalytic training is constantly rising. A large proportion of University appointments in psychiatric departments in the United States are held by psychiatrists who are also psychoanalysts.

Dr. O'Connor, in his book *Psychiatry: A Short Treatise*, writes:

> 'It must be conceded that, but for the stimulating and energizing work of Freud and of those who have come after him, we might still be blundering along among the psychiatric catacombs of last century.'†

* *Guardian.*
† J. Wright, Bristol, 1948.

Still more striking is the testimony of doctors Mayer-Gross, Slater and Roth in their monumental *Clinical Psychiatry*.* This is all the more valuable, since they do not like psychoanalysis and have succumbed to the emotional hostility that so usually infects such critics, and in places use language reminiscent of Eysenck. Nevertheless they have to admit 'the magnitude of Freud's achievement', and say that 'where previously there had been complacent nescience and even humbug and wilful self-deception, Freud brought realism, clarity, and a powerful technique of investigating motivation'.† It is striking evidence, however, of the extent to which emotional bias can be carried, that having put on record this clear appreciation of Freud, these authors omit all reference to psychoanalysis in the second edition of their book.

To cite a quite independent thinker: E. H. Hutten, a physicist of London University, in a searching paper 'On Explanation in Psychology and Physics' in *The British Journal for the Philosophy of Science*,‡ accepted fully the validity of the psychoanalytic method and type of theory-making as properly scientific within its own field of research, and points out that in different areas of reality scientific investigation cannot mean exactly the same thing so far as method is concerned. Thus Eysenck's assertion that all the experts have long ago ceased to take psychoanalysis seriously is merely not true. He is careful not to quote those who differ from him. This is propaganda, the principle of which was laid down by Hitler, namely that if you are going to tell a lie tell as big and brazen a lie as you can, and there will always be someone who will believe it. This is, however, not science. We cannot accept Eysenck's attempt to exclude 'our subjective experience of ourselves' as a proper field for scientific investigation by methods suitable to it. It is a fact fully as real as any conditioned reflex and to most of us far more significant. But we must, in the next section, examine some of the evidence which he alleges justifies negative conclusions about psychotherapy.

5. *Psychoanalysis as Science*

We may now proceed to a fundamental question. *What is really at stake in this conflict of views about psychotherapy?* Only in the light of the answer to that question can Eysenck's detailed criticisms be seen in their proper perspective. *If Eysenck could prove that psychotherapy does not take place, what would he really have proved?* There are, in fact, two separate questions involved

* London, Cassell, 1954.
† Op. cit. p. 24.
‡ Vol. 7, May, 1956.

here: (a) the suggestion that psychotherapy does not take place at this present time, and (b) that it cannot ever take place and is not possible. Let us see what is implied in these two views.

(a) If Eysenck is simply wanting to claim that psychotherapy is not achieved by our present methods and theories, then the only valid scientific inference would be that it is our scientific as well as humanitarian duty to go on working at it till we know enough to achieve the results we seek. If Eysenck said that he was not satisfied with the results at present achieved by psychotherapy, every analyst and therapist would agree with him. But he seeks quite plainly to discredit psychotherapy and rule out any further expenditure of time on it. He claims that there is no scientific proof of its good results, that it is a fiction and not a reality. In fact his claim rests on his own particular conception of psychological science and of scientific proof. He takes for granted by bold assertion that these are the only views possible and are everywhere accepted. Because, on his own admission, psychotherapy is not the kind of thing that can be easily fitted into his conception of science, he asserts that it is not scientific at all, and no good can come of it.

In fact, every worker in this field comes up against the problem of the exact nature of psychology as science. Freud came up against it at the beginning of his investigations. Trained as a physiologist and neurologist, he did his utmost for a long time to keep psychology strictly within the bounds of the kind of concepts used in 'natural science', the study of purely physical facts as in astronomy, physics, chemistry, physiology and so on. But ultimately, after making a major attempt in 1895 to work out a 'Project for a Scientific Psychology' in purely physiological and neurological terms, he abandoned the attempt as impossible. It was not that what Eysenck would call 'New Learning Theory' had not yet arisen to facilitate such an attempt. It was rather that *problems of meaningful and motivated action in man's experience of himself as a 'person'* were driving Freud to lay the foundations of a new type of scientific approach, the creation of *psychodynamic science*. Thereafter, though with reluctance, he was forced by the facts he was dealing with to evolve a new type of scientific terminology suitable to the study of man in his 'personal' life, and not just simply as an organism. I have made a detailed study of this in *Personality Structure and Human Interaction.** Those who are ill at ease when they get too closely involved in the disturbed emotional and personal life of human beings, will always seek to tie psychology down to the impersonal methods and ideas of 'natural

* Hogarth Press: The International Library of Psychoanalysis.

science', and will want a therapy based on 'techniques' rather than on 'human relationship'. Psychoanalysis began there, and it was Freud's courage in facing boldly the implications of his own discoveries of 'transference' and 'resistance' that forced him, in spite of his own preference, to open up a new path.

E. H. Hutten, the physicist already quoted, describes how physical science selects what is relevant to its point of view and thus simplifies the phenomena it studies. He then adds:

'The behaviour of human beings cannot be simplified in this manner; indeed, we should not accept an explanation that presupposes such a picture. Many stimuli act on us and our future does not lie along a single path. . . . In psychology the situation is not as simple as in physics where we have a single set of fixed *static* conditions and constant forces.'*

He goes on to point out that 'psychological' happenings are 'overdetermined', that is they have a plurality of causes or motivations, and the same set of data can lead to exactly opposite results. He proceeds:

'Classical physics is taken as a standard when it is said that a scientific theory must explain a given phenomenon in one way only; but this is not really true even there, and certainly not in modern physics.'†

He concludes that objections to psychoanalytic explanations as 'unscientific' are founded on a misinterpretation of scientific methods based on 'Newtonian Mechanics'. These do not apply to psychological facts and he adds:

'We must learn also to respect the diversity of subject-matter and expect it to influence the structure of a theory. Methodology may not be used for prescribing what science should be.'‡

That, however, is exactly what Eysenck does. He uses the type of methods of theory-making and testing which are valid in the 'natural sciences' and by means of them seeks to rule out of court the purely psychological investigation of our dynamic and emotional personal life which psychoanalysis carries on, and the

* 'On Explanation in Psychology and Physics' in the *Brit. Journal for the Phil. of Sc.* Vol. 7 No. 25, 1956, pp. 76-7.
† Ibid. p. 82.
‡ Ibid. pp. 84-5.

methods of therapy based on it. Thus his stock argument is that psychotherapeutic results are not proven and valid, because they are not compared with a 'control group' of similar patients who did *not* have the treatment. In a laboratory one can isolate two identical pieces of a chemical substance in stable conditions and bring a selected agency to bear on one and not on the other. Whatever change occurs in the first piece can then be regarded as due to that agency and not to anything else. But to have a genuine controlled experiment of this kind in psychotherapy one would have to have two groups of identical patients (which is impossible to start with), and they must have identical histories, environments (husbands or wives, families, circumstances, jobs, social status) and so on through everything that can affect our human lives. Otherwise changes in the patients cannot be really compared.

Eysenck loves to compare two roughly selected groups and discover that *symptoms* die down to about the same extent both in the group treated and the group not treated. But what has actually been happening to each individual patient no one knows, nor what is the exact state of mind of each patient, for *the disappearance or remission of symptoms is a most superficial criterion which skates over the top of all the important issues.* Eysenck makes his own task easy by selecting remission of symptoms as identical with cure and by choosing to regard a neurosis as 'nothing but' its symptoms.

Every analyst knows how seriously psychotherapy can be hindered by environmental pressures which are beyond control. Psychotherapy is not a single fixed entity and cannot be. It varies not only with the patient and the environment but with the psychotherapist. Two psychotherapists may have been trained to the same theoretical approach and yet be utterly different in their respective personalities, and they will make quite different impacts on their patients. On the other hand, I would expect a person suffering with an outbreak of neurotic illness but married to a stable and understanding partner, to 'get better' at least in the sense of achieving a 'spontaneous remission of symptoms' without treatment, at an earlier date than a patient could be helped by psychotherapy if married to a cruel and inconsiderate partner. The psychotherapist does not think of himself as carrying on his work with the patient in a vacuum. But this would invalidate one of Eysenck's typical control experiments, which would be even more completely disrupted by such a case as the following. A female patient who had had quite exceptionally cruel treatment as a child was, at one period of analysis, spontaneously reliving in an unconscious way during the night, some of the terrible scenes of cruelty to which she had been subjected. She knew nothing about this but gradually her husband and I were able to use the nocturnal rememberings to bring back to her conscious memory things that were troubling her and filling her with fear. In the middle of this process her husband suddenly and unexpectedly fell out of work, and for a few weeks the family had a most anxious time in their present-day life. Her nocturnal and unconscious 'acting out' of the past stopped abruptly. She said, 'I don't know anything about this, though my husband tells me it is so; but I expect I am too worried about him and our financial security to bother about my past.' Then the husband got another job, and automatically the nocturnal reliving of the past was proceeded with. Whether that had happened to a member of the 'treated group' or the 'untreated group' in one of Eysenck's 'controlled experiments' it would have destroyed at a stroke any real comparison between them. Human life is too complex and human nature too subtly individual for much faith to be put on experiments that must rest on rough averages, and the hope that with enough cases the accidental factors will cancel each other out.

How could a 'control experiment' be devised for a case like this. A man sought treatment for depression but also had had severe, recurring sinusitis for years. In analysis his talking centred more and more on his mother, though he never made any reference to her death. Then another sinus attack began to develop and he woke in the night in a panic with totally forgotten memories of her ghastly death-bed scene rushing back into consciousness. The next morning he came for an analytic session, went over the whole episode, and reported: 'As these memories were rushing back, at the same time my sinuses opened and pus and blood poured out. By morning it had cleared itself up for the first time without medical aid.' After that turning point, he improved steadily, and moreover has never had another attack of sinusitis. Not only has his physical and mental health improved but he has done what before he had never been able to do, get into the profession of his choice. His treatment has ended and he is carrying on stably. Eysenck's arguments would merely leave him unimpressed. Though this is an unusual case, analysts are familiar with sinusitis as a mask for depression, which lies behind the symptom.

It must not be thought that I am opposed to attempts at 'control experiments'. I simply think that the difficulty is to devise one that really means and proves something. The experiments Eysenck quotes in his paper in *The Handbook of Abnormal Psychology*, and on which he bases his negative statistical conclusions, have not much to do with psychotherapy in any fundamental sense, as I understand it. They appear to be attempts at 'psychological first-aid', carried out either by personal influence or intellectual interpretation which did not touch the deep causes, or get to grips with the enormous complexity of the emotional life of the human being. To me they prove, not that psychotherapy is useless, but that it is much more difficult than has yet been understood, that we have much more to learn about it, and that any attempts to state final conclusions about it are premature. I shall endeavour in the next chapter to state exactly what I mean by this.

Meanwhile it will throw some light on the problem of psychotherapy in general to take a look at the accounts of psychotherapy which Eysenck reviews. Space will not permit us to examine them all, but we will take the first three as samples.

(1) *The Cambridge-Somerville Youth Study* lasting eight years was divided into a treatment group and a control group, each having 325 boys who had been selected as likely to become delinquent. In the first group 'this large-scale treatment effort was directed at the prevention of delinquency, by guidance, counselling and therapy,' both psychoanalysis and the Carl Rogers Counselling methods being used. It was found at the end of eight years that rather more boys had committed delinquent acts in the treatment group than in the untreated group. Eysenck concludes that therefore psychotherapy is useless. From the point of view of real psychotherapy, however, the conclusion and the experiment alike are surprisingly naïve. It is just *not* the aim of psychotherapy to 'prevent delinquency'. The boys were apparently quite aware of the purpose of the 'treatment' to which they were subjected. Some of them said, 'It helped me to keep out of trouble.'* But the boys did not seek help of their own accord. They were selected as likely delinquents and 'as soon as a boy had been selected as a member of the treatment group, he was assigned to one of the counsellors employed by the Study and treatment begun.'

What would be likely to be the effect on the boys who had been so selected to undergo a 'treatment' designed to make them conform to the social rules? Young delinquents are rebels against the society which has given them a bad and disturbed start in life. It would not have surprised me if the occasional acts of overt rebellion had been markedly higher in those selected for treatment than in those who had been left alone. I am reminded of a patient who was sent to me by his employer after a brush with the police. Treatment was a condition of the continuance of his job. After a couple of years he appeared to have improved and stopped

* Op. cit. p. 703.

coming. A year later he wrote and asked if he could restart treatment, saying: 'Last time I came because I had to. I know my employer meant to help me and am grateful, and I felt you could help me, but I always knew I could not really accept it. This time no one is sending me; I'm seeking treatment of my own free will because I want help.' This voluntary treatment brought much more decisive improvement in his personality and led to promotion in his work.

Psychotherapy for the prevention of delinquency must be based on the idea of 'Adjustment' as a goal and criterion of mental health. Concerning this, Dr. H. V. Dicks, in his Address from the Chair to the Medical Section of the British Psychological Society, 1950, said:

'I find the concept of adjustment highly suspect. Adjustment implies that someone who has revolted and will not play the game according to society's rules must be brought round to accept his social obligations. Psychiatrists are often, not without reason, accused of acting on behalf of current social norms. Such people as sexual deviants, delinquents, etc. when they come for consultation with a view to treatment, sometimes express the fear that they would be levelled down to the norm. . . . I cannot regard normality, i.e. the average fitting into the current culture patterns, as synonymous with mental health. . . . Any therapy, individual or social, based on the conscious or unconscious strategy of moulding a child, a patient or a group, like a lead pipe till it fits, seems to be fraught with dangers. I am therefore deeply suspicious of the notion of "adjustment" and of the effects in the long run of all methods of suggestion, persuasion, and forcing also implied in some of the physical methods. To remove symptoms and to leave their meaning undiscovered is often to over-lay the issues, thicken repression and prevent growth.'*

All such important considerations as to what really constitutes psychotherapy are ignored by Eysenck. Delinquency is a symptom and true psychotherapy aims not at eliminating symptoms but at freeing the personality from the deep-seated anxiety which arrests natural development. That is a long-term process, and just as any other symptom is liable to revive at a time of stress during a long treatment, so would the symptom of 'a delinquent act' be liable to recur. This experiment was misconceived, and its statistical

* *Brit. J. Med. Psychol.*, vol. 23.

results which Eysenck reviews, have no bearing on the problem of what happens in psychotherapy.

The view to which I have been driven by what I find emerging in patients, is that the basic problem in psychotherapy is to reach and reverse the patient's hidden, fear-enforced withdrawnness from life, which was caused originally by the bad psychological conditions of early childhood. I know from practical experience how extremely complicated and difficult a task it is to secure the rebirth of the lost heart of the personality, and how much revival of intense early fear the patient has to face in the process. In fact, one of the ways in which human beings whose real rapport with their world is extremely shallow, try to force themselves back in touch, is the commission of acts of aggression. If these are treated as nothing but delinquent acts to be prevented, the individual merely feels that he is not understood and is being driven to fight all the harder for a personality of his own. Eysenck cites this Youth Study as a valid example of psychotherapy on the results of which he seeks to found a final negative conclusion of its effectiveness. In fact, it is only one of numberless experiments that have been going on to find out just what psychotherapy is. At present psychotherapy is not a finalized science but a still proceeding method of research, and we do not know what the psychotherapy of fifty years hence will be. All we know is that we are slowly contributing to it. Probably most of what is today called psychotherapy has not progressed very far beyond the aim of strengthening self-control. Even Freud defined it as 'strengthening the ego against the id', i.e. strengthening the self of everyday consciousness against the power of instincts. We are only just beginning to break into the deeper problem of the growth of basic strength in the personality, and we cannot be deterred by Eysenck's attempt to put a premature closure on the whole subject.

(2) *A Follow-up Study of War Neuroses* by Brill and Beebe. This is described by Eysenck as 'a statistical analysis of data collected during and after the war in connection with soldiers discharged from the army for neurotic disorders or returned to the army as cured.'[*] This illustrates the difficulties described above in deciding what is meant by psychotherapy in the given experimental field. Brill and Beebe concluded that, 'it appears doubtful if there was any difference in the effectiveness of the three gross types of treatment', i.e. rest and sedation, individual therapy, and hospital routine. Eysenck concludes that 'the effectiveness of psychotherapy . . . must be considered completely negative'.[†]

[*] Op. cit. p. 704.
[†] Op. cit. p. 706.

In fact the overall figures, it seems, showed that those treated by rest plus sedation and by individual therapy showed a higher percentage of cases returned to duty, than with no treatment or mere hospital routine. Nevertheless, no conclusions of a final kind about psychotherapy could be based on such data, for no information at all is given as to what actually constituted 'individual therapy'. Under wartime conditions were the therapists really trained and experienced therapists in all cases? Could they be when no general training in psychotherapy exists, and much that passes for psychotherapy is on an amateur level? Furthermore every experienced therapist knows that he does better with some types of patient than with others because of limitations in his own personality. Could this have been taken into consideration under the conditions of army psychiatry in wartime? Moreover, the same considerations apply here as to the Cambridge experiment. If the delinquent is not going to be moulded by psychotherapy to fit the culture pattern of society, neither is the neurotically ill patient going to be moulded by psychotherapy to fit into the culture pattern of a society at war which demands his return to the army.

We may quote Dr. H. V. Dicks again on this matter of regarding 'the average fitting into the current culture patterns, as synonymous with mental health'. He writes:

'Consider two major examples of the fallacies involved. The first concerns our activities in military psychiatry when we regarded the fitting into the norm as a favourable point in a man's history. . . . For many people fitting into the Army pattern represented a regression to a lower level of mental health which they had perforce to adopt, in order to meet this demand for soldiers from a crazy social system. Again, consider the cognate case of the demands for conformity made by a totalitarian system such as the Nazis. We know that the best "adjusters" to that pattern were not necessarily mentally the most healthy!'

In view of this, it would appear that in the above example it is not only quite uncertain what is meant by psychotherapy, but even uncertain what is meant by neurosis. Was a schizoid individual who did not break down because he was too detached mentally to be affected by what was happening around him, mentally more healthy than a sensitive man who could not tolerate the horror of war? Psychotherapy would be concerned with promoting mental health, not with fitting the individual to the wartime pattern. The statistics Eysenck relies on would only be capable of supporting the conclusion he seeks to impose on them if (a) psychotherapy were a known fixed entity, (b) neurosis were a known fixed entity and (c) every individual human being could legitimately be run into the same mould. None of these is true, and it is sheer loose thinking to try to base final conclusions on such flimsy and unspecific evidence.

(3) *The Barron-Leary Study* of 150 cases from the same clinic classified them into three groups, those receiving psychotherapy, those receiving group therapy, and those accepted for treatment but not yet having received any. The study only covered treatment of at most *under nine months duration*. The patients, though not so ill as to need hospitalization, suffered from such serious troubles as obsessive and schizoid characters and hysterical disorders. It appeared from examination of the patients at the beginning and end of the period, that 'changes in the treatment and non-treatment groups occur in very much the same fashion and in the same direction'.* Eysenck therefore concludes that 'this study would appear to indicate a complete failure of psychotherapy to produce any effects whatever'.† However, considering the three types of illness mentioned, we must observe that a schizoid problem underlies both obsessional and hysterical disorders. The unhappy schizoid individual has all his life been so withdrawn into himself that, though he may be able to 'think' in a highly effective way, he is unable to 'feel', and if he is once pushed out of his impersonal, intellectual or mechanical way of living, he encounters the most terrifying fears. It is the most difficult of all tasks in psychotherapy to help a patient to reveal and consciously experience the full extent of his 'withdrawnness' and then to stand by him while he outgrows the intense fears that force him to remain so detached from life. One of my patients recently said to me, 'You tried to help me bring this out a year ago, and I wanted to and tried, but you can't do this by trying, and I see that I just wasn't ready or able to then.' A study based, therefore, on less than nine months of treatment, appears to me to be quite unlikely to throw any significant light on the ultimate possibilities of psychotherapy.

On the inexact and highly limited evidence of these studies, the only sound conclusion is that most of what passes for psychotherapy is very superficial, and is likely to have as much or as little success as any other method so far as remission of symptoms goes. I am not, of course, saying that such limited studies ought not to be made. They are a challenge to complacency and are

* Op. cit. p. 706.
† Op. cit. p. 706.

probably the best that can be done at present by way of testing the results of all forms of treatment. I am simply saying that it is quite absurd for Eysenck to use them to support a *final judgement* of any kind about psychotherapy, let alone a negative one. Dr. E. Stengel, Professor of Psychiatry, Sheffield University, writes of Eysenck's contribution to *The Handbook of Abnormal Psychology*: 'He seems quite out of touch with present-day medical thinking and his knowledge of psychiatric history is faulty. . . . His criticism of psychotherapy has become a set piece which does not improve with repetition.' Concerning his view that neurosis is nothing but symptoms, Stengel writes: 'In this science fiction there is no such thing as "the patient" . . . only faulty organs and faulty habits.' *I do not think it matters much what methods are used for the alleviation of troubles when the real causes are not going to be touched; except that it is always preferable to use personal rather than impersonal methods.* Successes will be in the nature of 'First Aid' and will be produced by enforcing controls in some way. But control is not cure. Cure can only mean fundamental regrowth of the personality. It does not matter that at present we know far less about this than we would wish, for all our psychotherapy is an ever deeper probing into this problem. Psychotherapy has been evolving from superficial to deeper levels, and the psychotherapy most worth discussing today is that which seeks the way to a radical cure by getting at the basic causes.

Neurosis is not a collection of separate habits or symptoms. It is *the problem of the total self as a 'whole person', the sensitive heart of whose nature is withdrawn in fear from all positive relationship with the outer world. What is withdrawn is in particular the capacity for warm-hearted, open, affectionate, friendly relations, the basic human need to love and be loved.* In an unhelpful environment the child rapidly learns that if you love and need to be loved, you can be hurt. He becomes afraid to love and afraid to need love, and he grows up refusing to 'wear his heart on his sleeve' often to such an extent that the vital heart of his selfhood is taken out of circulation. He becomes a basically shut in person, living with only half a self on the basis of compliance, aggressiveness or, underlying everything else, detachment: but never feeling fully alive. Deep within himself he feels weak, and the contempt which our culture usually forces him to feel for his weakness, constitutes the first great obstacle in the way of psychotherapeutic attempts to help him. No psychotherapy, indeed no treatment of any kind, is radical, if it does not reach and reverse the patient's fundamental withdrawnness. I am unable to discover in Eysenck's work, whether it be in his criticism of psychotherapy

or his exposition of behaviour therapy, anything that contributes
to the solution of this problem.

(b) If, however, Eysenck seeks to prove not simply that psychotherapy does not take place now, but that it cannot ever take
place, then he is trying to prove that no human being can be
helpfully and healingly affected by another human being in a co-
operative personal relationship. I suggest that that is an absurdity
which reveals the fact that what is at stake is not the scientific
validation of psychotherapy at all, but the question of the philosophy of 'man'. Is 'man' a significant 'person' whose life has a
meaning and all of whose actions are intelligible, or is he only a
physiological organism whose reactions are automatic and often
accidentally originated habits, to be automatically reconditioned if
not useful. Eysenck is, it seems, stuck fast in the 'natural science'
philosophy of last century, and does not see that, when we study
the private individuality of the life of human beings as persons a
different conception of science is called for. Every patient is a highly
individual person, not a collection of meaningless accidental
habits. Psychotherapy is therefore highly individual and no two
patients can be treated exactly alike. The most important factor
in psychotherapy is undoubtedly that patient and therapist should
be capable as human beings of understanding each other. This
is what Eysenck escapes from by seeking an impersonal technique
which can be conveniently operated on all comers alike and called
'scientific'. *What strikes me most about his theory is its triviality
as an account of the human suffering involved in neurosis.* Compare his account of 'habit-breaking' with this dream of the patient,
quoted on p. 71, 'I was a lost child, crying for my father.' Her
history justified the dream, and she was flogging herself to exhaustion point in an endeavour to face life in an adult way while
feeling like that.

It does not follow, however, that because psychotherapy is still
in process of evolution, and as yet no easy means of scientific
validation of its results have been devised, that therefore it does
no good. Just as a new type of method and concept is needed to
study personality, so also a new method of testing must be arrived
at. Meanwhile the effects of psychotherapy do not depend on
their being proven. There are many much more subtle effects
than loss of symptoms, and these are the important changes. As
distinct from the dying down of symptoms with the subsiding of
tension (what Eysenck calls 'spontaneous cure'), the real undermining of symptoms only occurs through a gradual accumulation
of unconscious changes which are impossible to keep track of
accurately, let alone measure. One of the best ways I know of

estimating subtle changes which are going on in the structure of a personality, is offered by the patient who makes use of a favourite theme in dream or phantasy, and recurs to it at intervals in his analysis. Thus one patient had a passion for model railways as a boy. As an adult under analysis, he constantly recurred to model railway phantasies over a period of several years; each time the phantasies occurred, there was a small but significant change in them, and gradually it became clear that the whole series presented a fascinating pictorial or symbolic account of the stages through which he was undergoing a basic development of personality. The first phantasy was of an engine going round and round a single closed circle line in a little room. The patient was agoraphobic and experienced severe anxiety every time he ventured out of the house. Gradually the railway systems developed, became more complex, opened out into systems of communication far and wide, and finally ceased to be model railways and became phantasies of real railways carrying the busy traffic of real life. Stages in this phantasy series often predicted the next step forward which the patient was about to make in increasing his range of capacity to deal with real life situations.

Eysenck's statistical nets are not fine enough to catch such subtle effects of psychotherapy as this. Nevertheless they do occur. Emotional bias apart, what is really at stake here is the nature of science when applied to the study of psychological facts. Opinion, it seems, still differs here. Some regard the 'natural' or physical sciences as the only real sciences. One can look through a copy of *The Journal of Mental Science* and find almost nothing but articles on the physiological processes that are held to underlie psychic life. Others do not regard that kind of knowledge as genuinely *psychological* knowledge, so that if one turns to a copy of *The International Journal of Psychoanalysis* one will find nothing but articles on emotionally dynamic processes of our personal life, in terms of conflict, motivation and meaning. These two do not contradict one another or rule each other out; they should be partners in a joint enterprise of understanding human beings from every point of view. But the study of 'persons' must be free to evolve its own type of scientific method.

That it is really a question of the nature of psychological science which lies at the root of the criticism of psychotherapy, Eysenck really admits in a very odd way, in his book *The Uses and Abuses of Psychology*. On pages 224-6 he tries to draw an artificial distinction between 'understanding' and 'explaining', and is thereby trying to rule out the properly psychological study of man as non-scientific. He writes:

'Valuable and useful as it may be, psychological insight and understanding by themselves have nothing whatsoever to do with psychology as science. . . . From observation I venture to assert that many of the greatest psychologists are if anything below average in this quality of "insight" into human motives and purposes. . . . The psychologist knows no more about "human nature" than the next man, and if he is wise he will not let his claims outrun his discretion.'

I can well believe that that is true, and that it would be a good thing if such a kind of 'psychologist' had the 'discretion' not to venture on the discussion of psychotherapy. One would certainly not think anyone suitable to be a psychotherapist if he were 'if anything below average in this quality of "insight" into human motives and purposes'. Every psychotherapist has had the experience of a patient saying: 'You are the first person who has seriously tried to understand me, and that gives me some confidence in myself.' But when Eysenck says that psychological insight and understanding of human motives and purposes have nothing to do with psychology as science, he borders on the ridiculous, for motives and purposes are the very facts with which the science of the 'person' must deal. He is merely exhibiting his own preference for the kind of 'psychology' which avoids dealing with the 'person' in properly 'personal' terms, and for dealing instead with something more easily measured and managed by the methods of 'natural' or physical science. He writes:

'If the psychologist as a scientist is not trying to understand other people, then what precisely is he trying to do? He is trying to explain their conduct in terms of a system of general scientific laws.'

This merely begs the whole question. Dr. T. Szasz writes:

'Mathematics can function as a tool in physics and astronomy without the identity of those sciences suffering thereby. Psychology cannot so use mathematics without altering its own identity. . . . Attempts to make psychology more "objective" . . . run the risk that in so doing the subject-matter becomes altered and can no longer be considered to be psychology.'*

* 'Is the Concept of Entropy Relevant to Psychology and Psychiatry?' in *Psychiatry: Journal for the Study of Interpersonal Processes.* Vol. 19 No. 2.

Eysenck says that psychoanalysis tries to understand, not to explain, while his type of psychology tries to explain but does not understand. Most people will wonder how you can explain what you do not understand, and will feel that what is really understood is explained. A primary need of all mentally ill people is to be understood, in this case by the psychotherapist. Only so can the patient get a firmer hold on his own humanity and begin to feel more real as a person.

Eysenck evades coming to grips with such disturbing things as 'subjective' motives and purposes, and is confining his studies to habits, conditioned reflexes and responses, because they can be so much more easily fitted into his mechanistic notion of science. We do not dispute his right to study what he likes nor even that his line of study is a legitimate one. We only dispute his assumption that his line of study is the only scientific psychology, and his right to exclude from the realm of science what the psychotherapist studies, in ways and by means of concepts that are appropriate to our subject-matter.

One further point may be touched on. In the *Guardian* article Eysenck wrote:

'After over sixty years of psychoanalytic research the fundamental beliefs of the Freudians are still based on personal conviction rather than on scientific demonstration. That such demonstration would be *difficult* is universally agreed.'

That last admission is really a tacit recognition of the fact that science is up against a new kind of problem here. But how foolish to expect us to jettison psychotherapy because 'over sixty years of psychoanalytic research' have not yet enabled us to devise 'scientific proofs of results' that satisfy Eysenck's particularly narrow conception of scientific proof. Sixty years! If we go no further back than the Greeks, it took astronomy twenty-three centuries to find its Newton, and another two hundred years to find its Einstein. Future generations will not allow that a twentieth-century critic has disproved psychotherapy for all time. It is a remarkable attitude in a 'man of science' to try to exclude *any* aspect of reality from scientific investigation in terms appropriate to itself. Psychodynamic theory is only in its infancy. It is not a fixed thing but a growing exploration of personality in terms of what patients can tell us about themselves. I know of no psychoanalyst or psychotherapist who thinks the problem of psychotherapy is solved; but while Eysenck goes on rushing to the attack, psychoanalysts go on patiently trying to 'understand' human beings, to 'explain' them to themselves, and to stand by them while they grow out of the conflicts that make their lives a misery.

It bears on this question of the tragedy of neurosis, that Eysenck in the *Guardian* reiterated the claim that neurotics get better spontaneously without any treatment, and says that 'Denker put this matter beyond doubt once for all when he followed up 500 severe neurotics' for two to five years. It is an extraordinary claim that one such investigation should settle this matter once and for all. Of course, periods of acute emotional stress die down, but that is not a cure. When giving the broadcast talks from which *You and Your Nerves* originated, I received some 1,500 letters from listeners, a full third of whom wrote in these terms: 'I had my first nervous breakdown in my twenties and every few years since (ranging from two to five years) I have suffered a recurrence of the old trouble.' These letters gave periods ranging from ten to forty years during which the recurring breakdowns had gone on. Some of them had had hospital treatment, most of them only such treatment as their G.P. could give them. Moreover it was clear that in between these acute flare-ups of the trouble, these sufferers were still tense, anxious and unhappy people, and not in any genuine sense 'better'.

My own experience leaves me in no doubt which of the two types of treatment patients will prefer, if only adequate psychotherapy is available and its real difficulty and limitations in practice are honestly accepted. What all patients above all express is their lifelong and unsatisfied need to be understood and treated as 'persons' in their own right. Only then have they a chance to develop a stable and matured personality, however much this or that psychiatric treatment or behaviour therapy technique may suppress this or that distressing symptom. It is, then, to the problems of psychotherapy itself, rather than to its critics, that we must now finally turn.

CHAPTER TWELVE

THE NATURE AND PROBLEMS OF RADICAL PSYCHOTHERAPY

---

1. The Need for a Personal Therapy

WE must now gather up the threads of the whole argument, to pave the way for a closer consideration of the final problem. *This final problem is whether a radical regrowth of a badly disturbed personality is possible.* To approach this realistically, we must bear in mind certain facts which should have stood out clearly from what has been written in the earlier chapters.

(1) The problem of mental ill-health is far greater than all our combined resources to deal with it, and its causes are embodied in, and maintained by, the 'culture-patterns of insecurity' that hold us prisoner. They result in human beings coming at birth into environments quite unfitted to protect and nourish them emotionally in the first few vital years when the foundations of stable personality ought to be laid. The result is that all through the long story of mankind, the mental health of human beings in the mass has always been on such a low level, that none of the political, economic, social and ideological changes history has witnessed have ever been able to eliminate the chronic destructiveness on both large and small scales which leads men repeatedly to wreck their happiness and security. *Destructiveness is the most obvious behavioural symptom of mental ill-health,* and has always seemed so unvarying a feature of human life that it has actually been accepted by religious, philosophical and psychological thinkers as a biological innate instinctive drive. In point of fact, however, destructiveness does not characterize non-anxious and mature human beings. It is a product of fear and a sign of weakness. Its prevalence is an even more convincing proof than widespread neurotic illness of the fact that mental health is our No. 1 priority.

(2) In view of this, psychiatry is obviously called on to face an impossible task if it is expected to deal with 'mass mental ill-health' by the treatment of individuals. Psychiatrists know this and do, and can only do, the best open to them with limited knowledge and resources, to mitigate the sufferings of those individuals they have a chance to help. Mental ill-health is not basically a medical problem.

(3) Only within the last hundred years, for the first time in the history of mankind, has the problem of 'mental ill-health' begun to be faced fairly and squarely for what it really is. Previously it was obscured by the 'moral diagnosis' of failure to control natural antisocial impulses rooted in 'the flesh', and indeed the first scientific attempts to understand human nature accepted the same idea. At last it is beginning to emerge that *the real problem* is much deeper and in a sense more elementary: it is *the failure of the human environment to enable the infant to grow the basis of a stable personality in earliest childhood*. The responsibility for this cannot be put merely on parents, for they are themselves products of, and their limitations are due to, the same wide causes. We read in Exodus ch. 20 v. 5 that 'the iniquity of the fathers' is 'visited upon the children unto the third and fourth generation'. Always has it been recognized that individuals are caught in this vicious circle, but the investigations of psychodynamic science today lead us to formulate this truth also in another way. The *weaknesses* of the fathers are visited upon the children through *all* succeeding generations, unless we can ultimately create a world which is governed, not by power politics, but by a dominant concern for the mental health of human beings as rooted in the emotional security and positive development of personality in children.

(4) While prevention is a more important issue than cure, it is through attempts to cure that we have begun to understand the nature of the problem. But the psychiatric and psychodynamic sciences are so young compared with the most advanced natural sciences, that there has not yet been time to discover nearly all that we need to know, even to treat mental ill-health in individuals. All the various methods so far yield results of only partial success and partial failure. The optimistic propaganda of mental health programmes is very misleading and usually only presents the success side of the picture.

(5) While an increasing variety of physical and chemical methods of treating symptoms do enable psychiatrists in varying degrees to relieve suffering and to rehabilitate the mentally ill domestically and socially, these methods are not 'infallible cures' and they do not touch the real core of the problem in the mental structure of the patient's personality. For all that, we cannot possibly do without these methods, and in some cases even psychotherapeutic methods, which aim to deal with the personality itself direct, could not be used unless medical or psychiatric *control* of symptoms made the patient's states of mind more manageable.

(6) In the long run, however (and here I speak of what is ideally

to be aimed at, but is only practically possible as yet for a minority of cases), our goal must be to understand enough to be able to promote radical cures of the problem presented by the *ill personality* itself. Furthermore, cure depends not only on the possession of adequate knowledge, but also on the knowledge being used by human beings who have 'therapeutic' personalities, i.e. who really *care* for other people. This line of research is the special responsibility of psychodynamic science, of which Freud and the psychoanalytic movement must be regarded as the true founders. On this science must rest our methods of attempting psychotherapy, and we must stress again that the shortage of adequately trained psychotherapists is acute.

(7) Both psychiatry and psychotherapy must, in practice, choose between rehabilitation and cure as the aim in any given case. In most cases, but not in all, the issue is decided by the patient and the available possibilities of treatment. Probably most patients will be content with sedation and physical and social care while a remission of acute symptoms takes place through the silent working of the forces of nature. They will not want to seek any thorough-going changes of personality, even if the means to that end are available. But that is not by any means always true. I believe that increasingly, as understanding of these problems spreads, intelligent patients become less and less satisfied with symptom-relief, and feel a need for something more radical. This is what psychoanalytic therapy seeks to provide, though its development is as yet far from complete.

(8) From the point of view of personality, all methods which 'do things' to the patient without the full and understanding co-operation of that person (not just as 'agreement to submit' to some treatment, but as personal co-operation in a relationship which promotes normal and non-anxious development) could only be resorted to under the pressure of necessity. To base a mental health programme on impersonal techniques such as drugs, E.C.T., and reconditioning would discard all properly personal values. They are very present helps in a time of acute crisis, but the real aim should be to promote stronger and more mature development of the mental personality. I have even known some patients who resolutely refused the alleviation obtainable by drugs or E.C.T. They preferred to stick it out so that they might have a chance to grow slowly rather than submit to changes impersonally imposed on them. I do not think that that attitude is always wise or necessary, however, and may represent in itself part of a character problem; and it is not always possible anyway. But it still remains true that 'personal methods' are the most

desirable, and are the only ones that can promote the ultimate result we seek.

(9) We must then turn to the closer examination of psychotherapy to see whether it offers any real hope of reaching our ultimate goal. Some patients will even express a fear of being changed by the influence of another person in the free atmosphere of psychotherapy, which is very far from being plain sailing. All patients without exception experience a definite 'resistance' to treatment (as Freud first discovered) and take a long time to become convinced that the therapist is not trying to 'mould' them or 'make them change', but is only trying to help them to get free to grow in their own natural way. Psychotherapy means going along with a patient who is not content with quick symptom-relief at the price of remaining still the same fear-ridden person at bottom, but is prepared to grow in a healing personal relationship at whatever proves to be his own natural and possible rate of growth. In a good personal relationship, the impersonal techniques may be used as transient helps at times of stress, and may have to be so used, without harm to the patient's personal self-respect and integrity; but it is personal relations which are the important factors in the true development of personality. *Psychotherapy is the search for a personal therapy.*

2. *The Age Factor in Psychotherapy*

We have said that psychotherapy, like psychiatry, has to choose between the short-term policy of rehabilitation through the suppression of symptoms, and the long-term attempt at cure through the regrowing of the personality. The ultimate objective can only be cure. The difference between them is rather like that between the strengthening of the superstructure of a house which has no adequate foundations, and building in the foundations. In psychological terms, the difference is between training and discipline of the conscious self of everyday living, and a regrowing of the suppressed inner self which still carries the hidden legacy of the weakness and fear of a disturbed childhood. It may well be asked whether such basic regrowing is possible at all, once actual childhood is passed, and we must examine that question presently.

Meanwhile it is as well to mention that the choice between these two aims is not altogether a free one. The patient's age has a great bearing on what kind of psychotherapeutic aim he can tolerate or co-operate with. Broadly speaking, patients between the late teens and the early thirties are dominated by the drive to establish their independence of parents and build up their own separate position, career and home. At such a time, it is especially hard to find and admit weaknesses in oneself. The child within is intolerantly denied or treated with contempt. If psychotherapy is accepted at all, it is usually used to boost the conscious ego. Problems of childhood and of past and present relationships with parents are of course talked out, but with the general attitude of its being a good thing to disentangle oneself from all that and achieve greater independence. This is very evident in the case of patients in the twenties who succeed in the course of treatment in breaking away from a too-smothering home to get married, whilst at the same time developing greater ambition and venture-someness in their work. At this period of life, patients on the whole want therapy to support their workaday and social self against the undermining effects of the child within, rather than to have the whole legacy of childhood brought to the surface to be worked through.

I have had several patients who had several years of analysis in the twenties and established themselves with much more self-confidence in their everyday life, and then broke off treatment feeling that it was time they now stood on their own feet and got along without further help. Though the therapist may realize that there are still sources of insecurity in the patient's personality that have not been at all fully dealt with, the patient may well be right to suspend analysis if he feels he has reached a point at which he can carry on, and give all his energies to the consolidation of his position in life. He knows that if he feels he is slipping, the therapist is there to return to. The above mentioned patients returned to analysis either in the late thirties or early forties, and I had the chance to realize how different is the psychological situation at that age. Instead of a prevailing atmosphere of needing to strive ahead, there is rather an atmosphere of carrying a heavy load. Their positions in life have been achieved, responsibilities have piled up on them, domestic and financial stresses as well as the pressures of their work all combine to make them feel both tied and strained. The struggle now is not so much 'to achieve' as 'to keep going'. From deep down within, the anxiety-ridden child is emerging in a more recognizable way, and analytical therapy can be carried on at a deeper level. On the other hand, if, at this period of life, the child within is being more plainly forced into consciousness, the patient also has much more to support him in facing his inner problems. Those things in his life which are felt as burdens, also constitute his securities and incentives to solving these inner problems. He is, furthermore, more mentally developed than in the twenties and is more capable of facing himself without disguises, if he can find adequate help to go through with the painful process.

Something like this distinction must have been in Carl Jung's mind when he spoke of 'youth' as lasting from puberty to around thirty-five or forty, and said that

'Its significance . . . undoubtedly lies in the development of the individual, our entrenchment in the outer world, the propagation of our kind and the care of our children. . . . Money-making, social existence, family and posterity are nothing but plain nature—not culture. . . . Could by any chance culture be the meaning and purpose of the second half of life?'*

Without exactly adopting Jung's way of putting it, I think it is broadly true that in the twenties our aims are more concerned with our external world and from thirty-five onwards it is both more natural and more possible to turn attention inwards to whatever problems are emerging in our 'self', not in a superficial but in a quite fundamental way. Probably the age of thirty-five is generally the best age for beginning a really deep-going analysis which envisages a radical regrowing of the inner core of the personality, in so far as it has been cut off from development in infancy and early childhood. These age distinctions must not be taken as absolute, but as having a broad relevance to some of the difficulties which beset psychotherapy.

3. Psychotherapy and the Environment

I have already given some examples of how psychotherapy can be obstructed by an untoward environment. If a surgeon sets a broken limb in plaster, he expects that it will be left alone to heal and not interfered with by the patient's family. No such immunity from interference with psychotherapeutic treatment can be guaranteed. A patient's partner in marriage may seek to sabotage the analysis, by making the patient feel guilty about it. 'It's all right for you. You get help. I have to manage my own emotions as best I can.' 'What are you telling the doctor about me?' 'You'd get better just as quick if you told me all about yourself. I don't like your making a stranger your confidant.' The problem can become acutely difficult in the case of a patient in the later teens still living at home with parents. One of the parents may well be so afraid of appearing in a bad light, that the patient may be subjected to an interrogation at home after every session, and perhaps

* C. G. Jung, *Modern Man in Search of a Soul*, London, Routledge, 1934, p. 126.

even the treatment be stopped. The earlier tendency to blame the child for everything has rather given way to an opposite indiscriminate tendency to blame parents for everything, and that invites the reaction I have mentioned. It is also not good psychotherapy simply to teach a patient to blame parents. That will simply worsen relationships in real life and further add to the patient's insecurity. Blame of any kind should be replaced by the attempt to understand in psychotherapy, and in any case the difficulties of the parents have always been just as great as those of the patient. Psychotherapy is not a success unless it leads to better mutual understanding in all the main relationships of life; nevertheless, there are at times members in the patient's family who can make it nearly impossible to arrive at such a result.

If a patient's environment is just too bad altogether, whether at home or at work, it can make psychotherapy extremely difficult for another reason. The cause of the patient's problems seems now to lie so obviously in his external world, which is keeping up an unceasing anxiety-producing pressure on him, that he cannot accept the fact that his own inner emotional make-up contributes anything. In fact the aggressive person has already decided things that way, and blames everyone else for all that happens, thus escaping the necessity of knowing his own inner life accurately. Psychotherapy has its best chance when the patient's environment is reasonably supportive and understanding. It is not a treatment that works automatically.

4. The Patient's Resistance to Treatment

In the last two sections I have stressed two obvious difficulties encountered by psychotherapy, to pave the way for the consideration of a much more subtle one, which in truth brings us face to face with the hard core of the problem. It is so often a welcome relief to be able to blame everything on to the environment, just because it does arouse such legitimate and intense fear to have to recognize sources of weakness in one's own personality. For the same reason, the younger patient, who is so conspicuously at that time of life when he must prove capable of making his way in the world, has the strongest of reasons for not wanting to admit that there is anything wrong within himself as a person. The tendency to reach premature conclusions that one is now 'cured' or can 'carry on' is entirely understandable. Nor does this tendency, in fact, exist only in younger patients. Though it does vary with age, and also with type of personality, it is there in every case. It is *the attempt to reach the desired result of a*

*strong and non-anxious personality by a speedier route than is
possible, through resort to an impatient and often angry self-
forcing as a substitute for natural growth in security.* In some
form or other the patient feels it is weak to depend on the therapist
for help in things that concern his own personality, and that he
ought to be able to do it all himself. A simple but subtle example
of this is found in a patient who was a seriously neglected infant
during the first year of life. She had experienced a resurgence of
the chronic fear, weakness and dread of everything which had
characterized most of her early childhood, and felt a natural
enough longing to be able to grow out of all that more quickly
than she seemed able to do. Her quiet but slow progress was
suddenly halted by a marked increase of anxiety, and then she
revealed that she was becoming obsessed with phantasies in
which either her husband or myself were ill, and she had just
got to manage on her own, and was rushing about in imagination
doing everything by herself and fearing all the time she would
collapse. She was trying to put pressure on herself in this secret
way to 'go it alone' and only succeeded in delaying the real if
slow progress she was in fact making.

So far as my experience goes, the resistance to treatment which
Freud discovered is due to the inevitable continuance in the
patient's mental make-up of the policy he was driven to as a
child. Because he could find no one who really understood his
fears and anxieties, and for the most part only met with moral
exhortation to 'behave himself' or 'pull himself together', he had
no choice but to try to get along without help. He had to 'bring
himself up' in this inner sense. The only way he could do this
would be to develop an attitude of intolerance towards anything
in himself that seemed to savour of weakness and childish insecurity. Thus he could not avoid developing a dual personality; a
suppressed, frightened child self, being in part denied and in
part mercilessly driven on by the more obvious conscious self
struggling to meet the demands of everyday living. The more ill
the patient has become, the more clear is it that this civil war in
the mind is exhausting him, and yet the more convinced he is
that if he once relaxes his self-driving, he will collapse altogether.
He must keep going under his own steam, for he is certain that
if he once stops he will never start again. The more clear the
signs become that in a part of himself he feels an intense desire
to escape from it all, in the extreme case an actual longing to
regress to the helplessness of infancy, the more frightened he
becomes and the more likely he is to drive himself to that very
result by trying to increase still more the mental pressure he exerts

on himself. He becomes unable to relax or rest or sleep, unable to stop thinking or working or rushing about in various activities, and certainly unable to 'give in' to his need for a therapist to help and protect the terrified child that he is inwardly. From this basic conflict comes that resistance to psychotherapy which is the source of all the major difficulties in treating personality problems, and I believe it to be the source of most of the hostility to psychotherapy among its critics. People have been taught by our whole cultural set-up to despise weakness so much that they will do their utmost to avoid admitting it in themselves, or to hide it and refuse help for it if they cannot evade its inward recognition.

All this makes it clear that *the fundamental problem in psychotherapy,* and in life, is not the earlier idea of the demand of biological instincts for satisfaction but *the utterly necessary struggle every human being must put up, once he has had a bad emotional start in life, to achieve and maintain a self, ego, personality or whatever term one finds most useful, which shall be adequate to life's demands.* The struggle becomes so ruthless that the claims of the 'injured child in the unconscious' to be understood, protected, supported, and cared for, so that another chance can be had to grow a natural self, are rejected in favour of what are in fact self-persecuting techniques which inhibit all normal development and break down the whole self at last in neurosis or worse. Fear of the loss of personality becomes the driving force tending to bring about that very result. Troublesome sexual and aggressive impulses at least enable an individual to feel strong; what is really feared is the legacy of infantile and early childhood fear and weakness which is masked and buried behind problems of that order.

5. *Is Basic Regrowth of the Personality Possible?*

Investigation of this problem is, I believe, the most important research task of psychotherapy today. That patients under analysis themselves realize in some deep and inward way that this is what they need, is clear from dreams which approach the problem, sometimes negatively and sometimes positively. Thus one patient who had determined to pursue the negative policy of having no feelings and developing instead a life of trained practical activity from which all private emotion was excluded, had the following dream just before she stopped analysis only a little while after she had begun it. 'I had covered the entire surface of our garden with a layer of concrete, and set up a number of stone statues of human beings.' The dream plainly expressed the purpose of suppressing all truly human living and replacing it by a cold 'personality of stone'. The interesting thing is that the dream was an implied admission that treatment by psychotherapy would involve a process of growing, akin to the upspringing of new life in a garden. Another patient who had pursued his analytical treatment over a number of years and had worked through the more obvious conflicts of a sexual and aggressive nature which lay behind his symptoms, had this dream. 'I was digging up the bottom of my garden, to prepare it for replanning and replanting.' This dream has a forward look towards new development and occurred at a time when he was experiencing a conflict between feeling that the task was beyond him and he'd better 'call it a day', and feeling that he must go on and wanted to be able to live a fuller and more satisfying life than heretofore.

Another way in which patients betray their inward awareness of an unused, hidden and undeveloped part of their whole self, is in dreams of the following kind: 'I went into a locked room in my house and to my surprise it looked as if it had never been entered for years. Everything was covered up and thick with dust. I did not know what to do about it and came out.' Another such dream shows the element of fear in the situation. 'I was frightened to go into a dark room in my house and hurried away from it.' As the patient talked of the dream, it appeared that she was not afraid of something she thought might be in the room; her impression was that the room was empty, dark and that if she got into it she might never get out again. Patients who go deep enough in their analysis to get behind the actively disturbing dream and phantasy life of a sexual and aggressive kind out of which the painful physical symptoms come, in my experience always and consistently arrive at this stage. They complain of feeling shut in, out of touch, of being unable to get out of themselves, or to feel or express anything real. The physical experiences which go with this are feelings of being suffocated or smothered, of all physical exits from the body being blocked as in constipation or blocked sinuses and always the general state of tiredness and exhaustion and lack of interest. It is a general condition of devitalization in which they will say, 'I feel less than half alive,' or as one male patient constantly remarked, 'I feel like death warmed up'. This state of body and mind, of course, varies at different times, and one can always detect the existence of another part of the personality that has for years been dedicated to frantic attempts to force the withdrawn part of the self into action. When it is helped to emerge in analytical treatment, patients will say: 'Fear rushes up in me. I feel afraid of everything, like a small scared helpless child.' Then above all the patient needs to have a complete trust in the therapist to have a chance to grow out of this legacy of a disturbed infancy and achieve a rebirth of the natural, healthy self.

It is the main task of psychotherapy, I believe, to carry on psychodynamic research into this problem. Psychodynamic science is the study of man's wholeness as a person, in terms of what life means for him, and what motives, harmonious or conflicting, prompt and sustain his reactions whether they represent mental health or ill-health. This study has gone on for centuries in a pre-scientific way, but as a systematic scientific enquiry it really dates from the work of Freud. It has, like all scientific enquiries, gone through stages of development and is still very much in process of evolution. Because this science of the 'person' is still incomplete, the problem of psychotherapy is still unsolved. Psychotherapeutic practice and scientific knowledge must advance together in this matter.

While I can find no scientific or humanitarian interest in the efforts of some to discredit psychotherapy, I have no wish to make exaggerated claims for it. I have sought to show that I believe it is only now coming upon the most serious of the problems it seeks to solve. Having devoted a quarter of a century to psychotherapeutic endeavours to relieve human suffering, I have experienced all the doubts and disappointments that inevitably await workers in this field. I have had some failures, and some outstanding successes in lives literally reconstituted in health, domestic life and work, while the remainder showed varying degrees of improvement. This is the experience of every therapist. What, however, I always felt concerned about was that we know all too little about why the failures failed, why the successes succeeded, and what really goes on in the depths of the human mind to account for changes or failures to change in the structure of the personality. It was this dissatisfaction, which is shared by most workers in this field, that prompted me to make a close study of the whole development of psychodynamic science from Freud to the present day.* I was looking for emerging trends as pointers to future development, bearing in mind that theories are always in process of being reshaped by the direct evidence of what patients have to say. Freud's original biological psychology of instincts and controls was challenged, mainly in America, by a psychology giving priority to the influence of 'culture patterns' in shaping personality. Meanwhile in Britain a new and deeper analysis of the inner mental world of the individual from infancy

* The results of this have been set forth in the book referred to, *Personality Structure and Human Interaction*, the Hogarth Press.

onwards grew out of the work of Mrs. Melanie Klein, the originator of play-therapy for children. This was developed still further in a large-scale revision of theory by Fairbairn of Edinburgh, who shifted the main emphasis where it most certainly ought now to be put, not on 'depression' but on the 'schizoid problem' of the withdrawn personality.

I have already indicated something of what this has involved and must now make it more explicit. Two strongly developing trends became apparent.

(1) The first was the progress of psychoanalytic investigation beyond the problems of sex, aggression, guilt, moral conflict and depression, into the earlier and more deeply buried experiences of primary infantile weakness, dependence, fear in face of too much pressure or too much neglect, and the consequent development of a powerful fear-motivated flight from life, a defensive withdrawal into the self, and often into the deepest unconscious depths of the self, at a very early age. This leads to the formation of 'schizoid', 'cut off' or detached personalities whose emotional contact with the life around them is very shallow, and who seem to be incapable of much depth of feeling. If they have intellectual or other gifts they can achieve much in practice, but only so long as they can keep their lives relatively impersonal. They have little capacity for genuine human relationships. This problem, of the real heart of the self having become withdrawn in fear, underlies all other problems, whether of psychosis, neurosis, crime and delinquency, behaviour disorders or character problems. These more active problems arise in the course of the frantic struggles the withdrawn person makes to fight his way back into contact with his outer world. I have found that if psychoanalysis is carried far enough, it is always in the end the patient's fundamental *withdrawnness* that one comes upon. I have no doubt that in many people there is a specific 'withdrawn self' in the depths of the unconscious, of which they know nothing directly. As it is approached, it sets up the fear that the rest of the personality, the active self of everyday living, will be drawn down into the 'lost self', while consciously what remains is a state of fatigue, failure of energy and interest, and devitalization. Thus, one patient who was afraid to be alone in a room with the door shut, woke from sleep once with the feeling of having been down into an absolutely dark abyss in which her mind seemed to be a total blank, and she felt 'blind, deaf and dumb', and in a mental prison she could never get out of. She called out aloud to her husband for reassurance, and in session said to me: 'I can't get out of this by myself. You'll get me out, won't you.' There could be no more

impressive example of the fact that in the long run the 'cure' of mental ill-health needs a 'personal therapy'.

People whose true nature is imprisoned deep within their unconscious mental life by early intense fears, will find themselves unable to enter into loving and friendly relations with their fellows. If they cannot find a way of stabilizing and mechanizing their personality by means of some intellectual or practical way of living, they will be driven to exploit such naturally active capacities as sexual drives and aggressiveness in their struggle to keep in touch with their world and so keep their own personality in being. People would rather feel bad than weak, would rather feel angry than isolated, and would rather have bad relationships than none at all; for in a social vacuum we tend to lose our sense of our own self-identity. My experience is that the most difficult of all psychotherapeutic tasks for both patient and therapist is to reach and secure the healthy rebirth of the withdrawn core of the self. It is because of this that the results of psychotherapy have been open to criticism as uncertain and incomplete. The major task now confronting psychoanalytic research is to find out how to secure the release from deep-seated fear, and the healthy redevelopment in active self-confidence, of the patient's primary natural self which has been overlaid by the human mishandling of the years. We have almost everything as yet to learn about this, though something important is already known. Dr. D. W. Winnicott's view on 'therapeutic regression' concerns the finding of the way back to the patient's lost 'true self' to secure its re-emergence.

(2) The second main emerging trend I found was closely related to the foregoing. It was a gradual shift of emphasis from the parts to the whole in the study of 'man'. Gradually instincts, mental mechanisms, defences, symptoms, habits and so on, are dropping into the background, while in the foreground emerges one thing, the strength or weakness of the ego or 'whole personal self', the presence or absence of an adequate sense of stable and confident personal identity, the struggle to achieve and maintain a proper personality when the foundations have not been soundly laid. The fact that psychoanalysts have moved beyond the neuroses to the treatment of accessible psychotic persons has had a major bearing on this trend, for it is in the psychoses (the insanities and borderline cases) that it becomes most strikingly apparent that it is not the details of the patient's illness that are important, but the overall fact of his desperate and panic-stricken struggle to hold on to a personality, an identity, a self, while really feeling at bottom that he has not got any such thing. He

fears that he is breaking up or collapsing into utter helplessness
or becoming irrevocably shut up in himself or fading out into
nothingness.

Freud at first made modest claims for psychoanalytic treatment. He regarded it as only suitable for what were called the
'transference neuroses', the emotional illnesses, such as hysteria,
obsessions and anxiety states, in which the patient is still capable
of a personal relationship as a human being with the analyst. He
is then accessible to treatment. It was then held that those
suffering from psychosis (melancholic, paranoid and schizophrenic
states) were inaccessible and were not capable of forming any
emotional transference, i.e. any redirection to the analyst of the
repressed feelings of childhood for parents, and that it was not
possible to carry on psychoanalytic treatment with them. This
view, however, has been very greatly modified. It is now realized
that, though psychotics are apparently totally withdrawn from
any mental contact with the real outer world, and live to all
appearance completely inside a private phantasy world of their
own, in fact many of them are secretly quite aware of their outer
world, but are so terrified of it that they dare not venture out
into any kind of relationship. Yet to those who understand their
predicament, it is possible to help them to a sufficient feeling of
security to release them for human relationship once more. They
venture forth like a tiny, terrified child hidden inside a physically
adult body, and if they are violent it is their reaction to the
extremity of their fear. What is plain is that it is their 'whole self',
their personality in its entirety, that has been basically arrested in
development. It is not their instincts, their symptoms, their
defence-mechanisms, their habits that matter: it is the condition
of their essential 'self'. This problem which emerges so clearly in
psychosis, is in fact present, if in lesser degree, behind all other
types of mental ill-health. It may be disguised by being turned
into bodily illness or struggles with over-stimulated 'instincts', or
hidden by a façade built up by the use of marked intellectual or
other abilities, but an anxious and weakened 'ego' is the root of
all the trouble.

It is significant that Dr. Gwynne Jones, in his account of
behaviour therapy, writes:

'No specific mention has been made of the treatment of psychotic patients: neither the writer nor any of his colleagues
has direct experience of such conditions.'*

* Op. cit. p. 779

The psychotic conditions call, not for a behaviour therapy, but for a whole-personality therapy; and when the implications of this are fully recognized, it is seen to be equally true in the end of every form of mental ill-health. Unless human beings are dealt with as whole persons, no radical progress will ultimately be made with the problem of mental health. Any treatment that deals only with symptoms, habits, or particular tensions and conflicts, and does not come to grips with what is wrong with the 'self' as a whole, is superficial, however useful and indeed necessary it may be on a short term basis. It cannot be expected to yield radical and permanent therapeutic results.

Psychoanalysis itself has certainly not yet succeeded in securing such results but it is aiming to do this fundamental work. It may be said that one of its chief discoveries so far is just how difficult radical psychotherapy is. The classical or first stage of psychoanalysis cannot legitimately be criticized for not having produced final therapeutic results, for no one knew how deep and complex was the problem which Freud, following on from the earlier hypnotists, began to open up. The pioneer cannot discover everything. The early analysts carried out the investigations which first made it possible for later analysts to go deeper. Thus we may say that so far, psychoanalytical therapy has been provisional and transitional. It has led, in whatever degree it was successful, to better 'control' of the deep hidden sources of trouble in the personality. This was Freud's own view, stated in his extremely important late essay on 'Analysis, Terminable and Interminable'. It was a matter of bringing help to the hard-pressed 'ego' in its struggle to master the dangerous forces in the background, which Freud thought of as instincts. But once 'instinct theory' began to be questioned, the way was opened for the emergence of the real problem, that of the basic formation of a strong ego or else the lack of it. *The ultimate issue facing psychotherapy today is the issue of whether, if a basically strong ego was not formed in childhood, its lack can be remedied by any therapeutic procedure in later life.*

The following passage by Dr. Gwynne Jones has an important bearing, not only on behaviour therapy, but on the whole question of the scientific study of human nature and mental ill-health, and the therapeutic methods based on it. He admits that behaviour therapy does not take account of the 'wholeness' of the patient as a personal self. He writes:

'Another characteristic of this approach is its apparent disregard of the holistic* nature of a patient's personality. The investigations and treatments described were all concerned with partial aspects of the patient's functioning, and, in several instances, the aspect studied was apparently unrelated to the complaint which brought the patient to hospital. This is not to deny that an individual is unique, nor that, in certain respects, one deals with and 'knows' another individual in holistic terms. Description and measurement are, however, impossible without attempting to analyse the personality into its partial aspects . . . the art of a psychologist may be in his ability to deal with individuals, but his science consists in analysing the complexities which go to make up individuality.'†

I would, however, use Dr. Jones's words in another way and say that the art of a *psychotherapist does* lie in his ability to deal with individuals. On the other hand his science lies in conceptualizing the patient's wholeness as a person. The only kind of scientific knowledge which can aid him is *not* a 'science which consists in analysing the complexities which *go to make up* individuality' (present writer's italics) but a knowledge of the individual as a basically unitary self. An individual is not *made up* of his complexities like a collection of parts. His wholeness is the basic fact about him, and his primary concern is always to preserve it. Whatever pathological complexities come to exist within it are but signs of the ways in which he is a disturbed 'whole' struggling to 'pull himself together', in the popular phrase. These complexities cannot be separated out and treated in isolation as if they had nothing whatever to do with the 'person' whose complexities they are. They are the ways in which he is struggling to preserve his 'essential selfhood'.

I can well believe that many who read this will be inclined to say, 'this is a completely egocentric theory' and to regard that as sufficient ground for rejecting it. It is usual for other people to give good advice to those suffering from neurosis in the form of exhortations such as, 'You think too much of yourself. You ought to forget yourself and think more about other people for a change.' Such moral critics know nothing of the terrors of depersonalization and other kindred experiences of 'loss of one's ego'. Fear intense enough to cause mental withdrawal in infancy, when the child's relations with the outer world are anything but securely developed as yet, and his own inner self is anything but

* Holism: 'Tendency in nature to form wholes that are more than the sum of the parts by creative evolution.' *Concise Ox. Dict.*
† Op. cit. p. 780.

strongly formed, precipitates him into ever deepening isolation inside himself. As he grows up, it is of little use telling him to 'think more about other people'. He has lost the basic capacity to get into proper relationship with other people, and with it he has lost the sense of his own reality. Life becomes, in serious cases, one long struggle to keep himself mentally in being at all. Only if the therapist can get in touch with him in his inner loneliness, and overcome his fears, can he discover himself to be a real person and become capable not only of 'thinking' but of 'feeling' for other people. *Psychopathology is about the struggle to possess a 'self' to live with.*

We saw how Eysenck seeks to rule out psychotherapy and substitute for it a scientific therapy which deals with only habits and symptoms, 'bits and pieces' of the person. Wordsworth said of science: 'We murder to dissect.' Psychiatry, when it takes up emotional problems, is inclined to explain them as due to entities called 'patterns of reaction' acquired in childhood; and it is often simply assumed that if these are brought out into full consciousness they will be soon outgrown. Freud himself began with this supposedly scientific view that the individual is 'made up' of the parts, aspects, or what not into which logical analysis splits him up for the convenience of our thinking. Psychoanalysis is today beginning to outgrow this inadequate kind of scientific approach. It has emerged not speculatively but clinically that *the basic fact about the human being is his struggle to achieve and maintain his integrity and strength as an individual person in his own right; and the basic psychopathological fact is the survival in the physically and intellectually adult person of an emotionally, developmentally arrested child, withdrawn in fear and hidden in the unconscious. Radical psychotherapy can be no other than the attempt to secure the rebirth and redevelopment of this original 'natural self'.* If this problem is not yet solved, at least enough positive progress is made with some patients to show that a solution is possible. I will therefore, finally, consider two questions. First, ought this attempt to be made, or at least are there not cases in which it is inadvisable to probe to the depths of mental life? Second, if the attempt is made, what main phenomena do we come upon?

6. *Ought Psychoanalysis to Probe the Personality to the Bottom?*

There are certainly some critics who regard the entire psycho-analytical process as dangerous, and as more dangerous the deeper it goes. An ounce of fact is worth a ton of opinion on such a matter, so I would simply reply to this, that I myself had some-

thing over a thousand sessions in my training analysis, and I have
no doubt at all that the results have been beneficial. No danger
is encountered in the process that would not be liable to break
out of its own accord sooner or later under the stress of real life,
and then often at a time when there is no one by to understand
and help. Probably none but analysts realize how impossible it is
to force out of the unconscious what the patient is not going to
let out anyway, or not without careful emotional preparation.
There is likely to be more danger in releasing the unconscious
suddenly by means of drugs, than slowly by psychoanalysis. It
was Freud's view that you cannot artificially raise in analysis problems that life itself is not bringing out. But I think every psychoanalyst would agree that there are persons with whom deep
analysis ought not to be attempted. It is foolish to insist on perfection in things human, and it is obviously true that under certain
circumstances certain individuals succeed, in spite of a most disturbed childhood, in building up highly effective defences against
their deep down tensions. Signs that this is the state of affairs can
be discerned, and they have to pay a price of internal strain
for the stability they maintain. But they are able to maintain
themselves in a state of stable efficiency and good enough human
relationships for all practical purposes, and lead successful
lives which are not devoid of genuine satisfactions. So long as
their defences hold, no one would dream of attempting to disturb
them by psychoanalysis. In the same way as some people develop
such a stable defensive position in the ordinary course of growing
up, so no doubt some patients are able to reach a point of relative
stabilization after some amount of analysis and it is then unwise
to try to push analysis deeper. The case for deep analysis is
presented when the patient cannot find a sufficiently satisfactory
life without it.

These things are more easily made understandable by concrete
examples, and I shall take the case of Anthony Trollope as a
striking example of the building up of a magnificently effective
superstructure of personality on what must have been extremely
shaky foundations. Born in 1815, the first twenty-six years of
his life were years of almost intolerable unhappiness, as his *Autobiography* makes plain. At that age, solely to escape from the
miserable drudgery of clerkship in the London Post Office, he
accepted the position of clerk to an Irish post office surveyor at
a salary of £100 a year. He says:

'Nobody thought I was right to go. . . . I did not think it
right even myself—except that anything was right which would

take me away from the General Post Office and from London.'*

His father and a sister and brother were dead. His mother and elder brother were abroad. He had been found a job in the G.P.O. 'through influence' because he literally could do nothing else. His 'education' at Winchester and Harrow was a complete farce and he was untrained, and, it seemed, unfitted for anything. In 1841 he landed in Ireland 'without an acquaintance in the country and with only two or three letters of introduction from a brother clerk in the Post Office'.† A deeply depressed and lonely young man of twenty-six, with no proved abilities and an insignificant job in a strange land, must have had every reason to feel hopeless about his future.

Twenty-six years later, in 1867, he had so established himself as a novelist while carrying on his post office work, that he was able to retire from this public service, having 'put by enough to give me an equal income to the pension to which I should be entitled if I remained in the department till I was sixty'. Neither had he done this by neglecting his official duty. He had become a P.O. Surveyor charged with the responsibility of opening up and extending new postal services at first in Ireland and then back in England. So great did his ability prove to be that he was employed in negotiating postal treaties abroad, and carried on his writing while travelling for that purpose, for example to Egypt and America. He had risen to the highest ranks in the service, and was paid the compliment of being asked to undertake the American negotiations in Washington a year after he had retired from the service. Between the years 1847 and 1879 he earned by his writing just short of £70,000. Though not in the absolutely top class of English novelists, his down to earth realism, and his powers of observation, description and story-telling have assured him a permanent place in our literature. His Barchester series of novels hold a permanent place, and his six 'political' or 'Plantagenet Palliser' novels run them close. Of his 59 books, probably as many as twenty are still read today and are in steady demand in libraries. He died at the age of sixty-seven, in 1882, his last two books being published after his death. If we compare this success story with the utter tragedy of his first twenty-six years, we are obviously challenged to try to understand the 'how and why'.

Let us go back to look closer at what he had to overcome, and then see by what means he was able to accomplish this. Though both his parents were of outstanding ability, he grew up with

* A. Trollope, *Autobiography*. Oxford University Press, pp. 61-2.
† Ibid. p. 62.

almost nothing of what we would today consider to be adequate parental care. His parents are best described in his own words. Of his father he wrote:

'I sometimes look back, meditating for hours together, on his adverse fate. He was a man, finely educated, of great parts, with immense capacity for work, physically strong very much beyond the average of men, addicted to no vices, carried off by no pleasures, affectionate by nature, most anxious for the welfare of his children, born to fair fortunes—who, when he started in the world, may be said to have had everything at his feet. But everything went wrong with him. The touch of his hand seemed to create failure. He embarked in one hopeless enterprise after another, spending on each all the money he could at the time command. But the worst curse to him of all was a temper so irritable that even those whom he loved the best could not endure it. We were all estranged from him, and yet I believe that he would have given his heart's blood for any of us. His life as I knew it was one long tragedy.'*

While Anthony was a baby, the family moved to a farm at Harrow, after the father had ruined his professional career as a barrister by his violent temper. Anthony writes:

'That farm was the grave of all my father's hopes, ambition and prosperity, the cause of my mother's sufferings, and of those of her children, and perhaps the director of her destiny and of ours.'†

While he was at school at Winchester (his father's old school), his mother went to America to try to found a business to retrieve the family fortunes, being joined later by the father. At school, both at Winchester and Harrow, his life was utter misery, a social outcast with no money, despised by both boys and teachers. It was the practice then to leave much of the tuition of younger boys to older boys and he was thrashed unmercifully every day. His college bills were left unpaid and the school tradesmen would not supply his ordinary needs. He writes:

'My schoolfellows of course knew that it was so, and I became a Pariah. It is the nature of boys to be cruel. . . . I suffered horribly! I could make no stand against it. I had no friend to

* Ibid. pp. 31-2.
† Ibid. p. 2.

whom I could pour out my sorrows. I was big, and awkward, and ugly, and, I have no doubt, skulked about in a most unattractive manner. Of course I was ill-dressed and dirty. But, ah! how well I remember all the agonies of my young heart; how I considered whether I should always be alone; whether I could not find my way up to the top of that college tower, and from thence put an end to everything?'*

After three years of this life at Winchester, his father returned and set up home again at Harrow, where Anthony was now placed as a day-boarder. Having to walk three miles to school he often arrived unkempt, and was again without money or friends, and despised by all. Of this time, aged 15-18, he writes:

'My tutor took me without the fee; but when I heard him declare the fact in the pupil-room before the boys, I hardly felt grateful for the charity. I was never a coward, and cared for a thrashing as little as any boy, but one cannot make a stand against the acerbities of three hundred tyrants without a moral courage of which at that time I possessed none. I know that I skulked, and was odious to the eyes of those I admired and envied. At last I was driven to rebellion, and there came a great fight—at the end of which my opponent had to be taken home for a time.'†

This he calles the 'solitary glory of my schooldays'. Finally the father, though in broken health, had to fly the country for debt. From Holland Anthony returned to his first Post Office clerkship, in 1834, of which he says:

'I must certainly acknowledge that the first seven years of my official life were neither creditable to myself nor useful to the public service. . . . I think I commenced my quarrels with the authorities there by having in my possession a watch which was always ten minutes late. I know that I very soon achieved a character for irregularity, and came to be regarded as a black sheep.'‡

Here, surely, is all the making for an inevitable breakdown, sooner or later, into serious neurosis if not worse. He writes of the year 1841, when he was about to go to Ireland, the one move

* Ibid. p. 9.
† Ibid. pp. 12-13.
‡ Ibid. p. 44.

that proved to be the turning point of his life, that the first twenty-six years of his life were:

> 'Years of suffering, disgrace, and inward remorse . . . in truth
> I was wretched—sometimes almost unto death, and have often
> cursed the hour in which I was born. There had clung to me
> a feeling that I had been looked upon always as an evil, an
> encumbrance, a useless thing—as a creature of whom those
> connected with him had to be ashamed. And I feel certain now
> that in my young days I was so regarded. Even my few friends . . .
> were half afraid of me. I acknowledge the weakness of a great
> desire to be loved—of a strong wish to be popular with my
> associates. No child, no boy, no lad, no young man, had ever
> been less so. And I had been so poor, and so little able to bear
> poverty. But from the day on which I set foot in Ireland all these
> evils went away from me.'*

Could that be true, that *all* the evils springing from what he called
the 'crushing despondency of degradation' during his first twenty-six years, could utterly depart? In fact, it is clear that active
emotional tension remained with him all through his later life,
as we shall see. But first we must enquire what factors enabled
this man to stabilize his personality sufficiently to make such a
success of living, after such an utterly undermining and confidence-destroying start. Five things stand out as contributing to
this result.

Firstly, two hereditary factors, his great physical strength and
first-rate intellectual ability. These came to him from both parents.
His mother he describes as 'an unselfish, affectionate, and most
industrious woman . . . with high physical gifts . . . and much
creative power'. His history shows that he saw all too little of
her, both in childhood and adulthood. She lived in Italy for the
last nineteen years of her life, and before her husband died a
penniless debtor in Holland, she discovered a gift for novel writing
and supported the family by it. Her first novels were produced
while she was nursing a dying husband, son and daughter in
Bruges. Anthony writes:

> 'Her power of dividing herself into two parts, and keeping her
> intellect by itself clear from the troubles of the world, and fit
> for the duty it had to do, I never saw equalled. . . . My mother
> went through it unscathed in strength, though she performed
> all the work of day-nurse and night-nurse to a sick household.'

* Ibid. p. 60.

Her first novel was written at the age of fifty, and when she died at seventy-six she had published one hundred and fourteen books, which, though they may not live today, were quite best-sellers then. Thus Anthony certainly inherited great gifts of bodily strength and intellectual ability from both father and mother. It was his bodily strength that enabled him at last to subdue his tormentors at school in the great fight. It carried him, once he had established himself, through a life of quite extraordinary hard work and intense activity. He says:

'Few men I think ever lived a fuller life, and I attribute the power of doing this altogether to the virtue of early hours. It was my practice to be at my table every morning at 5.30 a.m.; and it was also my practice to allow myself no mercy. . . . By beginning at that hour I could complete my literary work before I dressed for breakfast.'*

The rest of the day was then free to be devoted to his work for the Post Office and his 'great recreation', hunting. That there was a very marked 'obsessional' element, as we would now call it, in his mode of working is clear. He describes it thus:

'Three hours a day should produce as much as a man ought to write. But then, he should have so trained himself that he shall be able to work continuously during those three hours—so have tutored his mind that it shall not be necessary for him to sit nibbling his pen . . . it is my custom to write with my watch before me, and to require from myself 250 words every quarter of an hour. I have found that the 250 words have been forthcoming as regularly as my watch went. . . . This division of time enabled me to produce over ten pages of an ordinary novel volume a day.'†

Thus he was always one, two or even three books ahead of his publishers. This is novel writing as an industry, not as an inspiration, and accounts for the fact that the obsessionally hard-working Trollope produced intellectually competent novels of a high order, but never achieved the magic power of the manic-depressive Dickens whose best work was bought at the price of periods of despairing depression when he could produce nothing.‡ The

* Ibid. p. 271.
† Ibid. pp. 271-2.
‡ Cp. *Charles Dickens*, Julian Symons, London, C. Baker.

internal tensions generated by his policy of 'having no mercy on
himself' in his intellectual labours, together with the physical
ardours of the enormous amount of travelling he did for the Post
Office both at home and abroad, took their toll, so that he died
of a stroke at the age of sixty-seven, when a man of his toughness
could certainly otherwise have lived to a very ripe old age. But the
great strength of body which enabled him to sustain all these
labours, gave him the chance to compensate for the deep misery
which was not altogether repressed in his mental life. Yet that
might not have been sufficient, had he not possessed the intellectual
gifts to make a success of what he did, for his mental capacity
took him to the highest ranks of the Post Office administration
as well as enabled him to write.

The second factor in his adult stabilization was his work. No
better piece of good fortune came to him than his recommendation to the Post Office. A friend of his mother was daughter-in-
law to the head of the G.P.O. and begged a clerkship for Anthony.
Though the first seven years were misery, his application for the
post in Ireland opened out a new life for him, a life of constant
travel usually on horseback which he loved. He developed a pas-
sionate attachment to the work of improving communications
for isolated districts and lonely people, and there is no doubt that
the driving force of his devotion to his work was a symbolic
compensation for his own early loneliness which still survived in
his deepest feelings. A job which consisted of constant travelling
on horseback was a tension-reliever to his restless and basically
troubled spirit, and constant meeting with lonely people and
with people of all sorts satisfied a deep craving in him for human
contacts. His work also gave him another great asset, namely,
freedom. In the nature of the case, he did not have to feel tied to
one spot, and was left to organize his own programme and time.
To one who, as a boy, had suffered so much from being in the
power of and at the mercy of other people, that freedom saved
him vexations that could well have broken him down had there
been no escape from them. As it was, he was always very intolerant of authority exercised over him by others, though to make
up for it the authority he wielded over himself in the name of
duty was absolute.

The third factor enabling him to preserve his personality as
an adult, was the result of this freedom to organize his own
time. He discovered a passion for hunting, and was able, without
neglect of his official duties, to hunt regularly for years. Though
he admits that he was not a good horseman, had bad sight and
was very heavy, yet he says:

'It has been for more than thirty years a duty to me to ride to hounds: and I have performed that duty with a persistent energy. Nothing has ever been allowed to stand in the way of hunting—neither the writing of books, nor the work of the Post Office, nor other pleasures. As regarded the Post Office, it soon seemed to be understood that I was to hunt . . . no word of difficulty ever reached me on the subject.'*

Clearly there was as much 'compulsion' about his 'duty to hunt' as there was about his obsessional hard-work in writing. Anthony Trollope was in truth, though a very kindly and sympathetic man by nature, one who could be quarrelsome and aggressive not only against 'authority' but in ordinary human intercourse. Hard work of an obsessionally self-driving kind, and bursts of aggressiveness, are common defences against, and accompaniments of, the struggle to keep going over the top of an undermining childhood. Much aggressiveness which would otherwise have broken out troublesomely in personal relationships must have been regularly 'worked off' in the hunting which he just could not do without.

The fourth factor that enabled him to keep going as a veritable human dynamo of work and activity for the forty-one years from his going to Ireland, was undoubtedly his marriage. He became engaged a year after his arrival in Ireland, to Rose Heseltine, whom he met at Kingstown near Dublin, the daughter of a Yorkshire bank manager. They were married two years later. During those first three years in Ireland he led a restless if jolly life, but could not bring himself to the steady industry required for writing, which he believed himself capable of doing. His first novel was finished a year after his marriage, his wife having been the only person to read it. She read everything he wrote from then on. Of his wedding day he says:

'Perhaps I ought to name that happy day as the commencement of my better life, rather than the day on which I first landed in Ireland.'†

The security given to this love-starved man by his wife, though with characteristic reserve about all intimate things he says little of it in his autobiography, merely observing that it concerned only himself and her, must have been of the finest kind. Of their

* Ibid. p. 64.
† Ibid. p. 68.

two sons, one, Henry, edited his autobiography, at his request, for publication.

One other, fifth, factor remains to be considered, for it was of exceptional psychological importance : namely, his novel writing itself. It grew out of a secret fantasy life which he developed as a boy, and which was at that time his only consolation in his extreme loneliness and misery. It was not the ordinary kind of compensatory fantasy which is common enough in childhood, by means of which children defend themselves against the frustrations of their inability as yet to achieve all they want to do. It was a fantasy life of an altogether unusually systematic and elaborate nature. An account of it must be given in his own words.

'I will here mention another habit which had grown upon me from still earlier years—which I myself often regarded with dismay when I thought of the hours devoted to it, but which, I suppose, must have tended to make me what I have been. As a boy, even as a child, I was thrown much upon myself. I have explained, when speaking of my school days, how it came to pass that other boys would not play with me. I was therefore alone, and had to form my plays within myself. Play of some kind was necessary to me then, as it has always been. Study was not my bent, and I could not please myself by being all idle. Thus it came to pass that I was always going about with some castle in the air firmly built within my mind. Nor were these efforts in architecture spasmodic, or subject to constant change from day to day. For weeks, for months, if I remember rightly, from year to year, I would carry on the same tale, binding myself down to certain laws, to certain proportions, and properties, and unities. Nothing impossible was ever introduced, nor even anything which, from outward circumstances, would seem to be violently improbable. I myself was, of course, my own hero. Such is a necessity of castle-building. But I never became a king, or a duke—much less when my height and personal appearance were fixed could I be an Antinous, or six feet high. I never was a learned man, nor even a philosopher. But I was a very clever person, and a beautiful young woman used to be fond of me. And I strove to be kind of heart and open of hand, and noble in thought, despising mean things; and altogether I was a very much better fellow than I have ever succeeded in being since. This had been the occupation of my life for six or seven years before I went to the Post Office, and was by no means abandoned when I commenced my work. There can, I imagine, hardly be a more dangerous mental practice; but I have often doubted whether, had it not been my practice, I should ever have written a novel. I learned in this way how to maintain an interest in a fictitious story, to dwell on a work created by my own imagination, and to live in a world altogether outside the world of my own material life. In after years I have done the same—with this difference, that I have discarded the hero of my early dreams, and have been able to lay my own identity aside.'*

This is a passage of extraordinary interest. Trollope's fantasy-life was quite clearly due to a schizoid withdrawal from the outer world which had become intolerable to him. How early this began we do not know. I think we must presume from his mother's affectionate nature, devotion in later years as the family nurse, and her great physical vigour, that Anthony was well mothered as an infant. Had he not been, it is difficult to see how he could have survived at all the extreme difficulties of his later childhood. Among his invisible advantages, we must reckon the foundations of security well laid in earliest infancy. But after that his world grew worse and worse around him, and he withdrew ever more into an internal world which he created in his own mind. Faced with specific mental withdrawal, this setting up of an inner world is an urgent necessity to save the ego, the personal core of the self, from, as it were, evaporating in a vacuum of experience. But he was right when he said that, 'There can, I imagine, hardly be a more dangerous mental practice.' So much energy can be used up in this inner world, that less and less remains available for living in the real outer world, and a progressive loss of touch with reality can develop and lead the way to neurosis and psychosis. The basic self is already fear-ridden, and the operative self of everyday living has less and less chance to develop efficiency in real life. A general sense of increasing weakness leads to ever deeper withdrawal to the fantasy life within. Behind this actively maintained inner fantasy world, lies hidden, a paralysed and passive infantile part of the self feeling helpless; though even deeper than that lies the primary active nature capable of re-development.

From this fate, Trollope was saved, I think, fundamentally by the security he experienced in infancy, secondarily by his great natural physical and mental vigour, and thirdly by the extremely practical way in which he controlled and organized his internal fantasy life. Had his early environment been a more possible one, it seems that he would have become a healthy, hearty extrovert

* Ibid. pp. 42-3.

enjoying life to the full. Since his environment was quite impossible, and refused him any possibility of living in it in normal human relationships, he created his own world in the mind. But he deliberately kept it as close as he could to what might have been outer reality. It did not grow into a totally subjective state towards which his normal conscious self was passive and helpless, leaving him, so to speak, sunk and bogged down in it. He ruled his fantasy instead of his fantasy ruling him. He took charge of it with steady intellectual effort, organized and directed it, kept it realistic and credible by insisting on rules of genuine probability. Thus, instead of drifting off into an hallucinatory and bizarre world of mental illness, he trained himself to keep his fantasy-life in close touch with real life, and in due course developed it into the art of the novelist. His physical strength and intellectual ability, his practical success in his Post Office work, and the support and companionship of his wife, all combined to enable him to develop his inner world without losing touch with his outer one. Had his marriage been unhappy, or had he been an unpractical and finally penniless failure in adult life as his father was, this intensive fantasy life could well have become more and more pathological. As it was, it brought him in hard cash, and his hunting was the exhaust valve of his remaining tensions—but not quite.

There remained in the personality of the successful adult Anthony Trollope some features that betrayed the presence of unresolved internal conflicts. He presented the typical combination of aggressiveness masking a deep need for love. He was driven on, even late into life, to hunt, when his sight was so bad that he could not see a fox nor recognize the nature of a fence, and was too stiff to vault on to his horse. But he says:

> 'I ride still ... with a boy's energy, determined to get ahead if it may possibly be done, hating the roads, despising young men who ride them, and with a feeling that life can not, with all her riches, have given me anything better than when I have gone through a long run to the finish, keeping a place, not of glory, but of credit, among my juniors.'*

In *The Eustace Diamonds* he says of one of the characters, Lucinda, that 'she likes hunting because she can gallop away out of herself'.

He was still fighting for a place among his school fellows in his deepest feelings, still struggling to prove himself to be somebody. He writes:

* Ibid. pp. 171-2.

'I wished from the beginning to be something more than a clerk in the Post Office. To be known as somebody—to be Anthony Trollope if it be no more—is to me much.'*

The experience of being an utter nobody as a child was there to be compensated to the end. One of his late-attempted but unrealized ambitions was to be an M.P., as a 'conservative Liberal', motivated practically by the pain it caused him to observe the cruel inequalities of fortune among men. He writes:

'It must, I think, be painful to all men to feel inferiority.'†

and there he wrote from the depth of his own heart.

This aspect of his make-up, however, showed through in other ways, such as his 'combativeness'. Of his work in the Post Office he writes:

'How I loved, when I was contradicted—as I was very often and no doubt properly—to do instantly as I was bid, and then to prove that what I was doing was fatuous, dishonest, expensive, impracticable! And then there were the feuds—such delicious feuds!'‡

His close friend, George Augustus Sala, wrote on the title page of his copy of Trollope's autobiography, 'Crusty, quarrelsome, wrong-headed, prejudiced, obstinate, kind-hearted and thoroughly honest old Tony Trollope.' (*Autobiography*, Preface, p. xiii.) Evidently, but for Trollope's basic strength and environmental supports, this legacy of his embittered childhood could easily have become predominant in his inner fantasy-life, and could have turned him into a persecuted, paranoid character who believed all the world to be against him. John Buchan wrote of him:

'He could understand the dark places of the human spirit, but especially he understood its normal sphere and the ordinary conduct of life. . . . He was perfectly conscious of the half-world of the soul and glances at it now and then, to indicate its presence, but he held that there were better things to do than to wallow in its bogs.'§

* Ibid. p. 107.
† Ibid. p. 291.
‡ Ibid. pp. 282-3.
§ Lady Tweedsmuir's anthology of John Buchan's writings, *The Clearing House*. Hodder and Stoughton, 1946.

He could not, however, prevent its vapours seeping through into his conscious everyday life, but he saved himself (in a way that his father was unable to do) from slipping down wholly into the bogs. There is one curious feature of his adult personality which shows that at some moments a sudden mental flight into himself from contact with his outer world would seize on him. In the middle of some crowded social function, a friend would find Trollope standing quite mentally abstracted, 'asleep on his legs', a peculiarity which was tolerantly accepted. One is reminded of the fits of trance-like absent-mindedness from which Tennyson suffered, which were undoubtedly a schizoid symptom and all of a piece with his shyness and his, at times, almost impossible domestic irritability and peevishness. In that generation these things were more tolerated as individual eccentricities. Today, we would have to recognize them as symptoms of mental illness which hide more dangerous possibilities, if once the individual's defences were to crack.

No analyst would dream of psychoanalysing a Trollope or a Tennyson while their defences held good, as theirs did. Behind it all, with Trollope, lay the one great basic unmet need for the secure loving personal relationships in childhood which would have enabled him to lay the foundations of an emotionally stable personality. He writes:

'I have long been aware of a certain weakness in my own character, which I may call a craving for love.'*

If Trollope could have been analysed, it would have been the business of his analyst to help him to recognize this as the legacy of his loveless childhood, and to accept it, not with depreciation as a weakness, but with understanding as a vital human need. That it must have been so well met by his wife must account for far more of his adult stability than we have the information to prove.

7. Is Self-Cure by Self-Analysis Possible?

We have seen that in favourable circumstances it is possible for a human being to 'contain and control' the legacy of even an exceptionally disturbing childhood. The total personality can evolve within itself a system of defences against its deep-seated emotional tensions. This may hold good and yet leave the operative self of everyday life free from over-rigidity, and able to adapt to and make use of all the possibilities that exist, or can be made,

* Op. cit. p. 159.

of living a useful and satisfying life. No one would risk disturbing this set-up by psychoanalysis, and greater tolerance and understanding socially of eccentricities that are not harmful to others will help. This state of affairs is not identical with full mental health and maturity, which very few possess, but it works sufficiently with the majority of us.

However, the fact is that in all too many cases life itself hits the individual harder than he can bear, and his mental defences break under a combination of internal tensions reinforced by external strains. Then the signs of more specific mental illness begin to develop. The question is often asked, 'Cannot a person do anything to help himself?' This question appears to be realistic and legitimate. It has, in fact, sometimes been given a more specialized form by raising the question of the possibility of 'Self-Analysis'. Several books have appeared on the subject. This would seem to offer many attractions, particularly to people who feel humiliated by having to acknowledge a need to be helped by someone else, and to people of an intellectual type who are used to 'mastering and solving problems by thinking'. They try to 'think out' the answer to their own inner problems, and if they do have an analysis will often come to session saying, 'I've been trying to analyse my feelings'. I well remember at the beginning of my own training analysis reporting a dream and starting to say, 'I think this dream means . . .' My analyst quietly remarked, 'It doesn't matter what you *think*, it's what you *feel* about this that's important.' That one remark as much as anything helped me to see and drop the defences of 'intellectualism', and to see at the outset that psychotherapy is a different sort of thing from 'thinking out a problem'. An 'intellectual', analysing himself, will be trapped permanently in this defence.

It will, however, be said that Freud analysed himself. There was no one to analyse the first analyst and he had no choice but to make his own mind his first laboratory (though it seems that later Freud and Jung attempted some mutual analysis). Freud gave us an account of some of his self-analysis. I think that, since the publication of Ernest Jones's *Sigmund Freud: Life and Work*, most analysts would now agree that Freud's self-analysis, resulting as it did in the emergence of the 'Oedipus Complex Theory', founded the modern science of psychodynamics, but it did not cure Freud's own neurosis. Nor does self-analysis ever cure. It simply switches one's energy over from emotional experience to intellectual activity. It enables one to become the detached scientific observer of oneself, and it has as little curative value emotionally as purely intellectual interpretation given by an analyst.

This is not just an opinion on my part but a comment based on personal experience. At one period I devoted considerable time to a determined attempt at self-analysis on the basis of adequate theoretical knowledge. It produced interesting intellectual but no practical results. Perusal of the literature of self-analysis confirms my own experience, if not the writers' own conclusions. Self-analysis may to some extent enable one to put up with one's own tensions better by understanding them, but even then it is open to the grave limitation of being at the mercy of all one's own 'blind spots' about oneself. A genius like Freud will see deeper into himself than most of us will, but a close study of Freud's theories show that his own 'blind spots' produced at some vital points rationalizations rather than objective scientific observations. It is agreed that one must be analysed oneself before one is capable of analysing objectively another person. Self-analysis, therefore, is parallel to analysis by an unanalysed person, and is at the mercy of the analyst's unconscious biases.

But ultimately the difficulty about self-analysis is even more fundamental. It resolves itself into this: the basic problem is the acute state of fear that holds in its grip an infantile part of the total self. Fear cannot be banished by being explained, but only by providing a new security for the frightened person. It is not 'analysis' that cures. That only pin-points the details of the total problem to which the curative agency must be applied. What 'cures', in the sense of providing for the patient an opportunity to regrow out of anxiety into self-confidence, is a new security-giving relationship with an understanding analyst: and in self-analysis that is just what is missing. In self-analysis one is still at bottom alone in a world of which one is fundamentally frightened.

If the curative factor is 'love' of a kind that should properly be called 'parental love', and intellectual *self-knowledge* does not solve one's inner emotional problems, it may well be asked: 'What about *self-love*?' There usually seems to most people something shocking about the idea of self-love, even though Christ told us to 'love your neighbour as yourself'. In fact, the question becomes a serious one in the light of the virulent self-hate many patients show, and which we mentioned in Part 1 (cp. pp. 47-8). Self-hate is obviously weakening. One young male patient after about a year's analysis said to me, 'One thing this treatment has done for me already, is to make me less hostile to myself.' It is much better to have an understanding and friendly attitude towards oneself than a contemptuous and depreciatory one. Some patients who have found little support in childhood from the adults round them, do develop a secret attempt to support themselves, as is shown by this dream: 'I saw a little girl in distress and she ran to me with outstretched arms, and I picked her up and comforted her.' The 'little girl' was a reassuring dream image of the patient's own childhood self, and she had been driven by loneliness to self-comfort. But the point here is that, though that is better than self-hate, it did not cure her. Self-love so usually develops in time into self-pity and in its turn undermines the personality further. Self-pity is a product of persecutory anxiety and a paranoid substitute for healthy self-love. The fact is that the healthy kind of self-love is only possible as a reflection of, an internalization of, the real, sound, objectively valid love of another person. My experience is that patients come to hate themselves all the more if they develop self-pity, and it is only through finding themselves genuinely valued and cared about by the therapist that they are able to shed their self-hate and adopt towards themselves an attitude that permits of healthy development of their true self.

Since these human ills are the results of bad human relations, it should be obvious that 'self-cure in isolation' is impossible in the nature of the case. A healing human relationship in the end is the basic essential. All that we can do for ourselves by our own unaided efforts in this matter, is to toughen up by self-discipline the everyday top-level of our complex personality, while leaving our hidden inner self in an all the more hard-pressed and anxious state. This may enable an individual to keep going so long as it does not end in 'nervous breakdown' as it so often does, but it is not a 'cure' in any final sense. One other point should be clarified. Intellectual self-knowledge must not be confused with the spontaneous development of *insight* into oneself. That is much more a process of intuitive emotional self-realization which the analyst's interpretations are designed to facilitate. Such flashes of insight into oneself constantly occur to a person who is moving and growing within himself, and they accompany and are essential to the full development of personality.

8. The Final Problem in Radical Psychotherapy

I have sought to make it clear that, in my judgement, the root cause of all personality disturbances is the degree of mental withdrawnness, due to primary fears, which has come to be a relatively permanent feature of the patient's personality. *Radical psychotherapy must consist of the alleviation of the primary fears and the reversal of this resulting withdrawnness, releasing the individual's full potential energy for growing and dealing with the real outer world.* To whatever extent fear and withdrawnness are

serious factors, people tend to live more and more in the inner
world of the mind, and as their detachment from outer realities
grows greater, their inner world becomes more and more a
bizarre anxiety-ridden fantasy world, easily recognizable in
dreams. The phenomena of dreams make it easy to understand that
there may be not merely a general tendency to be withdrawn, to
'go into one's shell', but a *specific and clear cut part of the total
self that is definitely withdrawn as a permanent characteristic.*
Its activity in dreaming may become quite lost on waking. The
more this is a fact, the more ill and crippled for real life the
individual is. I have called this part of the personality 'The
Regressed Ego', the part of the self that has 'gone backwards' to
escape intolerable pressures at too early an age. The whole dream
and fantasy life, both night dreams and daydreams, is a compensation for withdrawal from and lack of satisfaction in real life.
If real life in the outer world is satisfying, the child and the adult
does not need to create and elaborate a purely internal fantasy
world to live in. It is true that fantasy is normal in childhood in
that the child has to make up for his undeveloped and immature
hold on reality, of which as yet he knows all too little. But there
is a difference between normal fantasy which is an experimentation with life, and pathological fantasy which is a substitute for
living in the real world, even in childhood. Thus one patient, the
youngest of a large family, remembered as a boy sitting at table
lost in the fantasies he was weaving in imagination and resenting
any intruding claims on his attention, while the rest of the family
chattered noisily together. He was a sensitive child who could
not cope with the violence of the family group, which was disturbed as a whole by one psychotic parent.

But one can only find satisfaction in real life if one is in full
emotional touch with it, and the more one is withdrawn in one's
essential self, the more necessary it becomes to keep going a substitute inner world in order to keep one's own personality alive
at all. My experience of very deep analyses is that in the end this
inner fantasy life fades increasingly, and the patient is able to
come face to face with the two indubitably real parts of his personality, a self struggling to cope with the outer world, and an
inner hidden self locked away inside in a state of fear and helplessness. As patients become more directly conscious of the lost, shut
in part of their total self, they often experience it in the form of
fears of being imprisoned inside themselves and unable to get
out, feelings of being stifled, smothered, blocked up, hopeless.
Women patients often express this inner state of affairs by
dreams of childbirth in which the baby cannot be got out of the

womb. I often illustrate the position to patients by the analogy of Dunkirk. The Regressed Ego is like the British Army that withdrew from overwhelming opposition and went backwards into the safety of Britain, to rest and recuperate. The self of everyday living which still tries to carry on in the outer world, is like a bit of the army left to the desperate defence of a beachhead (as at Tobruk in the N. African campaign) and unable to draw any help from its exhausted and retreated other half.

The problem, then, is what is to be done about the Regressed Ego, in whatever degree, mild or severe, it exists. It is a part of the personality which was arrested in development at the early stage of the fear-ridden child or even infant. Though we speak of 'splitting of the personality', in fact no part of the total self can be absolutely and finally cut off. There is always an inner knowledge of apparently lost parts of the self. Nevertheless, in extreme cases it lies deep-buried in the unconscious and the patient keeps up the most intense resistance to its uncovering. Though he can never be a whole and healthy and fully active person until this lost part has been 'reborn', yet he fears every approach to it, because it seems as if its emergence will weaken and undermine the forced adult self he had struggled all his life to maintain. The patient himself is divided between wanting to recover possession of his whole self and, on the contrary, wanting ruthlessly to crush out the part of him that seems to be weak and an internal menace. For from it come all his anxiety-states and irrational fears, his suspicions of the hostility of the outer world, his feelings of exhaustion, devitalization, depression, lack of energy and interest, all his feelings of being inferior, little, weak, inadequate, all his longings to retire and escape from the pressures of life. One patient said, 'I don't know how I carry on at all. I seem to have no energy for anything and have to drive and drive myself all day long. There's only one thing that I can suddenly find terrific energy to do, and that is to rush to the library and get out half a dozen books to bury myself in.' The apparently devitalized and regressed person is not actually lacking in energy, but energy has been turned by fear into a backward drive for sheer survival sake.

This problem can be encountered in all degrees of severity, from mild to extreme, but it is the basic problem. Conflicts over antisocial impulses are secondary and arise as a result of the patient's struggle to fight back and counteract the drive to withdraw from life. Radical success in psychotherapy is not achieved until a patient's withdrawnness and regressive trend has been reached and reversed. But when we ask what is to be done about it, we find that psychiatrists and psychotherapists are as divided over the answer, as the patient is. Regression is feared as much by the person treating as by the person treated. Many hold the view that tendencies to regress must be firmly opposed and put a stop to, otherwise the patient is going to become helpless on our hands. The patient who begins to show regressive trends because at bottom he *really is* mentally exhausted by the struggle of a lifetime, must not be allowed to rest and recuperate but must be driven at all costs to keep going. Not all psychiatrists, of course, take this view, but probably the majority do.

Thus, in the *Nursing Times*, June 5, 1959, there is an article by a male nurse, Michael Dent, R.M.N., on 'Regression—a Problem in the Neurosis Unit'. It is explained that regression is a return to childish behaviour and is common 'whenever the environment becomes too much for the ego to cope with'. The writer points out that 'when the body is sick we take to our beds and allow others to take over our affairs', and that this is a return to a child-parent relationship. In fact when the body is sick, we have no option and may well die if we do not so 'regress'. But it appears from what the writer says that this sensible point of view is not to be extended to mental illness. He says: 'We have all met the exasperating behaviour of the more inadequate personalities among our patients. We call them "childish" and quite rightly for that is just what they are. The fact that a neurotic person is very prone to regression adds to the problem when treating neurosis.' This nurse then describes the organization of the unit at his hospital designed for the treatment of such cases. The patient (having of course found his own parents incapable of giving him security as a child) seeks to form a child-parent relation with the doctors and nurses. This must at all costs be prevented. There are five doctors so that the patient cannot become specially attached to any of them; the nurses are not called nurses because that would suggest that they are there to care for the patient, whereas the patient is there to be made to care for himself. In hospital the patient is, of course, 'under a strongly parental type of discipline. This is just what his maladjusted ego needs.' But it seems that parental love must on no account be given. He 'may discharge himself if he wishes to. Thus he does not feel that the "parents" are trying to delay his leaving home.' One would think that he is more likely to feel that the parents are anxious to get rid of him, which is in truth the case. He is an 'exasperating neurotic', and must be made to understand that it is no good looking to anyone else for the allaying of his deep-seated fears.

The writer states explicitly:

'The very title of "nurse" presents the picture of a capable person in whom one can confide and place one's trust. Therefore, titles are as far as possible dropped. The conventional uniform is also a symbol of security. . . . Thus in order to eliminate some grounds for regression the uniform is not worn.'

Evidently it is wrong to find someone in whom one can learn to 'trust', and nothing must be done to help a patient to feel 'secure'. The writer then adds:

'With all the precautions taken by the staff, still the patient tries to form a child/parent relationship with the nurse.'

Apparently this is done by trying to discuss his problems with the nurse, but this means wanting to be the favoured child and gain the ear of the parent. 'This form of primitive thinking occurs frequently in neurotics', and so the child must not be allowed to find a parent-figure capable of understanding him or helping him to understand himself. In fact all the sources of necessary security that were denied to the patient when he was a child must be denied to him all over again when he becomes an ill adult as a result of the first denial. I can well believe that under such a spartan régime, the patient, if he does not discharge himself, will appear to get well as quick as ever he can to get out of it. I have rarely read a more naïve and total misunderstanding of the problem of mental illness.

By contrast, I quote from a lecture given in the Leeds Department of Psychiatry by Dr. Brock Chisholm (Director, World Mental Health Organization). He gave as one of the typical problems in wartime psychiatry, the case of the tough Company Sgt.-Major, an old regular soldier who during several years of front line warfare had been the immovable rock on whom everyone leaned. Then he would get a trivial wound and be sent back to hospital, and as soon as he was in bed he would suddenly regress catastrophically to an infantile condition, crying, bed-wetting and soiling, slobbering and having small temper tantrums. Dr. Chisholm remarked that the nurse who knew her job, understood that this man had taken, over a long period, an amount of mental strain that had brought him to the limits of his endurance and it had become an absolute necessity for him to go back psychologically to the beginnings of security in the position of the child cared for by the mother. The nurse would pat and stroke him, talk soothingly to him, spoon-feed him and care for him, and gradually the strain would die away and presently he would begin to grow back to his normal adult personality. The hospital Neurosis Unit, whose treatment methods were described, apparently understands nothing of this need to make a therapeutic regression to get a new start in development. The male nurse's article ignored the fact that, quite apart from the disciplinarian methods employed, the fact that the patient was removed from the strain of life into a hospital at all constituted a permitted regression, and if the disciplined denial of all other securities had been attempted without at least that relief, the result would probably have been even worse breakdown. How much better to incorporate a proper understanding of the treatment of regression into the régime.

I quote Ralph Metzner (Psychologist, Harvard University) in his paper 'Learning Theory and the Therapy of Neurosis'* 'Virtually all "schools" of psychotherapy stress the warmth, permissiveness, acceptance, understanding, etc., of the therapist as an important factor. A study by Fiedler showed that the difference between experienced and inexperienced therapists on this dimension was greater than the difference between therapists of different schools.... Usually reality-testing [i.e. discovering that what frightened one as a child need not frighten one now] is performed solely at a verbal level. It has also been argued that a fear-response learned by a child in a preverbal traumatic situation can be reality-tested non-verbally by a sufficiently strong positive transference. This seems to be the function of the "love-the-patient" technique of approaching schizophrenics.'†

I do not doubt that it is possible to varying extents with different people, to force the repression of the need to regress, but at what ultimate cost? A case history given by the male nurse states that when the patient was last seen the improvement on discharge had been maintained; but that was only 'some months later'. The subsequent history of the patient we do not know. I had a patient who came upon a serious need to regress during the course of analysis. He had had a most exhausting childhood, was a man of very marked ability, a bachelor living alone, and the head of his own business. Under these circumstances he felt that it was impossible for him to let up on himself. He achieved by his own efforts, in turning himself into a highly organized professional character, the results aimed at by the above quoted hospital unit. No analysis could enable him to let go his defences. He would say, 'I have a business meeting next week I must be fit for. I can't let anything disturbing out just now' and so on. Finally he failed to arrive one session, and I discovered he had died suddenly of a

* Brit. J. of Psychol., Monograph Supplement No. 33. C.U.P.
† Op. cit. p. 22.

thrombosis. If he had had pneumonia, the business meeting would have had to wait, but he could not feel able to let it wait while his underlying mental exhaustion was attended to. Yet I have little doubt that, even if it had meant six months in hospital, a psychologically regressed illness at an earlier age would have forestalled the thrombosis, and probably added twenty years to his life. Those who advocate forcing the patient to repress the over-strained child, and treat him as an exasperating nuisance at all costs, do not take into account the long-term effects of the inevitable accumulation of internal tensions that must result.

For myself, I have come to concentrate more and more on exploring the possibilities of what Dr. Winnicott, a true pioneer of clinical progress, calls 'therapeutic regression'. This seems to me to hold the key to the solution of the ultimate problems of psychotherapy. Instead of letting the patient drift on unhelped till he cracks badly under internal stress, the aim becomes to contain and control his need to regress within the treatment situation. It cannot be taken for granted that this is always possible, and the more ill the patient is, the more likely it is that at some point, for a period, definite relief will have to be provided from the burdens of responsibility in everyday life. This is no more than is true for most bodily illnesses, and it is very likely that an inescapable need for a withdrawal for a time from the pressures of life is the deepest cause of many physical illnesses. Nevertheless, it is certainly my experience that a number of patients are fully able to bring their emotionally injured hidden child-self into their sessions of psychotherapy while maintaining, with gradually decreasing strain, their adult self in outer life. The dangers of regression in practice will be intensified if the need to regress is met with lack of understanding. I believe that the dangers of regression will also prove to have been exaggerated, when we have achieved a thorough analysis and understanding of the process, and have built up on that knowledge a constructive treatment aimed at making possible a radical redevelopment of the personality. This will only be done by therapists who do not make an authoritarian and disciplinarian approach to the patient, and do not take up the attitude of a busy parent defending himself against a troublesome and demanding child; but treat the patient rather as a human being who is struggling with decreasing success to carry adult responsibilities while at the same time hiding within himself a child-self who is exhausted and literally ill with fear. This also calls for mental hospitals where regression is not *repressed* but *treated* with the aim of securing a natural regrowth of personality.

My own experiences in seeking to help such patients, are based on trying to understand by analysis the self-exhausting nature of the patient's struggle to keep going. In so far as this proves possible, it also becomes possible to use treatment sessions as an opportunity for helping the patient to relax the pressure he puts on himself by facing the fears which make him feel he must keep it up at all costs. 'Relaxation-therapy' is useless if it is applied only to the body. The patient cannot relax properly bodily, until he is relaxed mentally. Bodily relaxation can be used as an approach to mental relaxation, and if that is done what usually happens is that just as the patient begins to feel relaxed in body, either sitting back in an armchair or lying on the couch, he begins to get restless, fidgety, and finds that his thoughts are gathering busily around some distraction or worry and that he cannot leave himself in peace, however tired he feels. Many people find themselves exactly in that condition when they go to bed at night, and do not realize that it is all part of their unremitting drive to keep themselves actively 'on the go' and defeat the secret undermining pull of the legacy of childhood within them. Patients usually do not realize how little able they are to relax until they try to do it in session, and the results provide many of the most valuable opportunities for true psychoanalysis of a fundamental internal conflict.

This kind of analysis brings out very clearly the fact that the most important conflicts that disturb human beings are not struggles to prevent themselves being 'bad' (i.e. antisocially sexual or agressive or both), but struggles to prevent themselves being 'weak', i.e. breaking down in face of the pressures of life. One finds that patients fear relaxation both because they feel they will lose their over-strenuous self-identity in the process, and also because they adopt pseudo-moral attitudes to it, describing it as self-indulgence, laziness and so on. One patient would repeatedly say, 'I feel as if I've never had a moment's relaxation, day or night, all my life'. The fact that a state of physical hypertension had resulted in a serious psychosomatic disease suggested that he was simply speaking the literal truth. This state of affairs begins in childhood. A simple example is that of a little girl with St. Vitus's Dance whose father shouted at her like a drill sergeant. The pressure put on the child was more than she could sustain. In such a predicament, the child can only struggle on, trying to drive himself to meet demands from which there seems to be no escape. In the process he develops a self in which he feels ever more weak and inadequate, and another self in which he becomes ever more intolerant of his own (and therefore of other people's) weaknesses, a self dedicated to the self-exhausting process of making himself keep going at all costs. In terms of our modern concept of 'ego-splitting', the first, weakened self is what I have called the Regressed Ego, and in its ultimate form it is the most deeply hidden part of the personality, both withdrawn and also kept repressed in unconsciousness, even though its results emerge into consciousness. The other, taskmaster or slave-driver self, the cause of all the phenomena of self-exhaustion and regression, can often be recognized in the form of a harsh, merciless and unloving conscience where it has taken on a moral guise. Freud invented a technical name for it, the sadistic super-ego, which he regarded as built up on the model of parents who, like the hospital neurosis unit, are so afraid of spoiling the child that they adopt a policy of discipline without affection. Fairbairn has substituted for Freud's term 'super-ego' a term which has a more precise meaning, 'anti-libidinal ego'. 'Libido' is the psychoanalytical term for the life-drive, particularly in the forms of 'instinctive needs' for everything that is essential to healthy living. Freud used the term more narrowly for 'sexual desire', Fairbairn uses it more broadly for our basic need for personal relationships of every kind, needs for everything that must come to us to nourish our personality from mother, parents and family, marriage partner, friends and colleagues, and the whole personal environment in the end. Thus in Fairbairn's sense, the term 'anti-libidinal ego' is a part of oneself in which one adopts an 'anti-needs' attitude, and it is surprising how widespread this is. Sometimes one discovers in analysis that the apparently most demanding and greedy person is so, because he is having to struggle against a most vicious secret attitude of denying almost everything to himself. In the end what is denied is every right and opportunity to relax and recuperate from emotional strains, with someone who gives a relationship of security. The patient quoted on p. 78 dreamed of sitting in my room feeling very worn and wanting to rest, and he discovered that another 'he' was standing behind the chair looking down on his worn and weakened self with hate and hostility and raising a dagger to attack himself. That is the state of affairs that underlies mental illness.

Long and detailed analysis is required to bring to light the exact detailed pattern and motivation of each patient's self-attack, and to relate it to his inability to relax and leave himself in peace so that his own 'nature' can have a chance to grow in spontaneous development. It is a long process because of the patient's real dread that, instead of regrowing, his personality may break down altogether if he once lets up on himself. Gradually it comes home to him that the opposite is the case, that he is breaking down because he cannot allow his own nature to know its own business and to 'heal in a state of rest'. I have seen very clear-cut manic-depressive problems fade away as the patients have at long last become able to allow themselves to be simple, unforced human beings.

I can well imagine that some readers will jump to the conclusion that this means the advocacy of an effete, spineless, self-indulgent attitude to life, one which, if it takes root in a civilization, soon condemns it to be superseded by so-called 'stronger and more virile' races. We must remind ourselves that we are dealing with mental illness, but even so this is undoubtedly a misunderstanding. We have only to contemplate the fate of Sparta in the ancient world, and the Nazi and Fascist movements in the modern world to see through this deception. These were cultures which despised love as weakness, and identified ruthlessness with heroism. They were the utter failures which, in their breakdown, have left nothing behind them of any value to mankind. The great contrast on the plane of history is the undying spiritual power of the figure of Jesus of Nazareth, based solely on the fact that he epitomized the essence of self-sacrificial love and care for the weak. I would make bold to say that the best definition of the attitude of the psychotherapist to the mentally ill is to be found in the words of Jesus: 'Suffer the little children to come unto me and forbid them not.'

Psychotherapy has thus two phases, first, helping the patient to relinquish his destructive inner self-attack, and second, after that, to foster the regrowth of his deep, fear-ridden child-self. One may say that in its first phase psychotherapy is a kind of 'Society for the Prevention of Cruelty to Children' but the children in question are inside, and are parts of, adult persons. When that is done, one cannot then just leave the child but must stand by him while he grows.

It is an astonishing fact how much even ill and very hard-pressed people can rise to an extra effort in a crisis. My view of the correct treatment of the mentally ill does not in the least rule out sacrificial effort, endurance, and heroism in critical situations. These are fine qualities, and we must not omit to recognize how much unappreciated heroism the mentally ill person is usually capable of in carrying on at all, under conditions which are far more difficult than more fortunate people are in a position to understand. Nevertheless, heroism and self-sacrifice are not usually prescribed for the treatment of any serious physical illness, apart from the heroism of holding on while the appropriate remedies are being applied. This must be our attitude likewise to mental illness. It does, indeed, take a great deal of moral courage and quiet, patient heroism, to go through with a long deep psycho-analytical treatment which reaches down to the fear-ridden depths of the personality. When the hidden disturbers of his peace have become conscious, the patient has no option but to live with them in a fully conscious way in order to gain the opportunity to grow out of them. What is buried in the mind is preserved. What is consciously lived through is kept in the 'growing area' of our experience. To have gone along, week by week, month by month, over several years, with patients who are holding on and some-how keeping going, doing a job or running a home while enduring what seems to them to be an almost unremitting state of chronic anxiety, is to appreciate why the patient needs the closest and most understanding support from his therapist; and it is also to appreciate ultimately the tremendous strength of the will to live, and the will to live as a real person, and the will to endure the discouragements and disappointments because progress seems so tardy, which patients show. Far more courage is needed to out-live and outgrow a neurosis, than to cope with the outer world with a fully vigorous and healthy personality. It is largely because of this, that when, slowly and in due course, signs gather of a permanent improvement of a fundamental kind in the patient's whole personality, one feels such thankfulness that psycho-therapy can 'get somewhere' after all.

I shall close with a piece of case history to illustrate the crucial point that what we are dealing with is 'total personality' not 'relief of symptoms'. The patient was a business man of quite outstand-ing capacity and success who, while he appeared outwardly calm, showed medical signs of strain owing to the ceaseless mental pressure under which he kept himself, and which he could not relax at will. It was his defence against the legacy deep within himself of an extremely undermining childhood. Very slowly, as this self-pressure relaxed, his physical health and mental happi-ness improved, but the intensity of the struggle is vividly ex-pressed in the following remarks, taken from sessions spread over a number of months. 'It seems that I've got a degree of human competence which is unusual, yet I feel whatever I do will go wrong. Yesterday I suddenly felt "Is all this a dream?" I've never felt quite real. If someone said "It wasn't really you who made the business go, you only went through the motions" I wouldn't feel surprised. It can be frightening being a person because then you've got to be responsible. Sometimes I feel it would be better to be nobody. So far I've been thinking of this analysis in terms of getting rid of bad things. But to become a positive person, able to take a lead and not always worrying over everything, seems like moving forward into a void. I can't imagine it.' Here emerged a basically withdrawn self, very much out of touch with his outer world. Against this he fought.

Later he remarked: 'All my life my objective has been, not to be myself, but to make myself something I am not. I'm sure this forcing myself to do things, finding something to do and making myself do it, is no good. I've got to live with myself as I am first. Often I feel tired out, yet I can't stop. I feel I've got to be doing something and don't really know what for. I spent years feeling cross, and felt nothing could alter it. Now I'm not cross that way, it's not the major thing it was; the major thing now is feeling tired, and so that feels it will never alter. I wake in the morning and find myself rigid in bed, my whole body held tight as in a straight-jacket.' One of his troubles was that he was constantly waking from sleep throughout the night. He said, 'If you only sleep an hour you have some confidence you'll wake up. You're not too committed, waking is not too far ahead. You've got to wake your self up to see how you're getting on.' One night he slept for seven hours and woke in a panic. He commented, 'If only I could relax a bit, but I feel I must be getting on with something. I think "Come on, get up and get on. You can't be lying about". I must be quick. Here in sessions I feel I stand over myself, saying, "Come on, get on talking; don't waste time!" I still do things with my teeth clenched. You say this sort of thing can't be hurried and that went home to me, but I think, "You idiot, all this analysis, it's time you got a move on!"'

Some clue to this terrible, persisting tension appears in the following. 'I take it as the natural order of things that children should be frightened of their parents, and everybody should be frightened of everybody else. It seems an odd idea that somebody should not be frightened. I feel fear is what makes the wheels go round. It keeps me at times worrying over the business. I use fear, to keep myself and others going. The first thing to do with a baby is to make it afraid, so you've got some control.' I naturally pointed out that the sort of control this gave him over himself was precisely what was exhausting him, and doing him serious harm. Fortunately he had reached a stage at which he could say, 'I am, however, now definitely less afraid and more interested in things. Anyone would have been frightened, brought up as I was.' Later at one session in which he had become quite relaxed and able either to talk easily or (what had always been more difficult) relapse into silence without feeling uncomfortable and guilty about not talking, he said: 'A year ago I couldn't have had a session like this, I'd have had to get cracking.' It is the psychoanalytic therapy of this type of problem which, I believe, holds the key to the restoration of mental health and release of all the dammed up energies of personality.

To summarize our conclusions, the centre of gravity in psychodynamic theory has shifted away from the idea of powerful instinctive drives of sex and aggression, and towards the recognition of the unconscious persistence of infancy fears, ego-weakness, and resulting dependence, as the root cause of all forms of personality disorder or mental illness. This calls for a reorientation of therapeutic outlook and technique. The basic drive in all human beings is the drive to achieve a viable ego, self or personality. This drive becomes dangerously distorted if the human environment arouses too much insecurity in the infant and gives too little constructive and loving human relationship.

The most tragic, albeit common product of this drive when it is distorted is *the horror of the hard exterior,* whereby a deeply insecure human being protects himself by the armour-plating of the so-called 'tough character', and then mistakes it for genuine strength of personality: while all the time the sensitive human heart of him cowers hidden inside, withdrawn into the unconscious, a terrified emotionally crippled child. It is out of this psychological set-up that all the horrible cruelties of man have arisen. Hitherto, man's capacity for inhuman cruelty has seemed to the majority of thinkers to be absolute proof of an ultimate evil factor in human nature. Theologians, moralists, philosophers, educationalists have practically always taken this view. Freud was convinced of its truth. In *Civilization and Its Discontents* he wrote:

'Men are not gentle, friendly creatures wishing for love . . . but . . . a powerful measure of desire for aggression has to be reckoned with. . . . *Homo homini lupus* (man is a wolf to man). Who has the courage to dispute it in the face of all the evidence in his own life and in history. . . . (It) reveals men as savage beasts to whom the thought of sparing their own kind is alien. Anyone who calls to mind the atrocities of the early migrations, the invasion by the Huns or by the so-called Mongols under Ghengis Khan and Tamerlane, of the sack of Jerusalem by the pious crusaders, even indeed the horrors of the last world-war, will have to bow his head humbly before the truth of this view of man.'*

* London, Hogarth Press, 1930, pp. 85-6.

However, we do not propose to 'bow our head humbly before the truth of this view of man', but must challenge it radically as a misreading of the facts. Brutality is man's reaction to insecurity. Man is dominated not by 'a powerful measure of desire for aggression' but by an absolute need to maintain his individual personality at all costs in a very insecure world, and to avoid breakdown while coping with the problems of everyday living. Anthropology and sociology today help us to understand how hardened patterns of insecurity get built into the persisting structures of community life in which every individual is shaped from birth. There is nothing that insecure human beings cannot be driven to in order to survive, unless they are so ill as to have lost the will to live. This is the source of the cruelties of human history.

Every race, nation, class and creed has produced this distortion of human nature. Perhaps the most frightful large scale example in history, making the Nazi concentration camps pale into insignificance by comparison, was the five hundred years history of the Roman Games, five centuries of a continuous publicly organized cult of inhumanity, blood-lust and sexual sadism and perversion, to amuse a degenerate populace for whom life had utterly lost all meaning. But the horror of the hard exterior emerged in the cold, harsh military discipline of Sparta (as opposed to the free spirit and cultural creativity of Athens): in the fanatical religious cruelty of the medieval Roman Catholic Inquisitor (as opposed to the all-embracing love of St. Francis of Assisi): and in our own times in the ruthless nationalistic militarism of the Nazis and the equally ruthless ideological militarism of the Communists. It is significant that Spartanism and Nazism died leaving nothing at all of any cultural or spiritual value to posterity.

What, however, is really of greater significance than these examples writ large on the pages of history, is the way this sinister tendency is discoverable in the daily lives of ordinary people, and indeed of our own selves. As soon as we feel threatened and unsure of our capacity to cope with the threat, do we not tend to go on the defensive at once in quite trivial situations, and get impatient, irritable, inconsiderate and bad tempered? It is only in proportion as the individual is basically secure and stable that he can cope with even the minor frustrations of everyday living without developing unnecessarily aggressive attitudes. From these mild beginnings every degree of pathological aggression motivated by fear can be traced. There is a healthy reaction to danger in which anger is over and done with as soon as the situation is dealt with. Basic insecurity gives rise to pathological states of fear, varying degrees of the paranoid suspicious mentality, and morbid obsessive sadistic aggression which has an element of desperation in it. The lowest common denominatior of our psychological troubles is the deep-seated fear, weakness and dependency of infancy when it has not been possible to outgrow it, and to hide which human beings can turn themselves into monsters in frantic self-deception. Behind this, their true human nature is locked away. Nothing is more sad than to see a human being facing his basic withdrawnness, and complaining with a terrible sense of frustration that he cannot express himself, cannot get in touch with other people, and cannot love. This is the problem to which psychotherapy must orientate itself.

BIBLIOGRAPHY

J. R. REES. *The Health of the Mind* Faber 1951 London.

NIGEL WALKER. *A Short History of Psychotherapy* Routledge and Kegan Paul, 1957.

J. A. C. BROWN. *Freud and the Post Freudians* London, Penguin Books.

S. FREUD. *The Psychopathology of Everyday Life* London, Penguin Books.

S. FREUD. *The Question of Lay Analysis* London, Hogarth Press, 1948.

> Of this book the translator writes: 'It will be mainly valued as the most masterly and attractive introduction to psychoanalytical knowledge; and the best answer to the question, "What shall I read of Freud?" '

K. HORNEY. *Our Inner Conflicts* London, Routledge and Kegan Paul, 1946.

H. GUNTRIP. *Psychology for Ministers and Social Workers* Independent Press.

H. GUNTRIP. *Mental Pain and the Cure of Souls* Independent Press.

H. GUNTRIP. *You and Your Nerves* London, Allen and Unwin, 1951.

H. GUNTRIP. *Personality Structure and Human Interaction* London, Hogarth Press, 1961.

PROFESSOR CARSTAIRS. *This Island Now* (Reith Lectures) Chatto & Windus.

CHILD PSYCHOLOGY

J. BOWLBY. *Child Care and the Growth of Love* Penguin Books, 1953.

GWEN CHESTERS. *The Mothering of Young Children* Faber.

SUSAN ISAACS. *The Nursery Years* Routledge and Kegan Paul, 1932.

AGATHA BOWLEY. *The Natural Development of the Child* London, Livingstone 1960.

AGATHA BOWLEY. *Problems of Family Life* London, Livingstone 1948.

D. W. WINNICOTT. *The Child and the Family* London, Tavistock Publications Ltd. 1957.

D. W. WINNICOTT. *The Child and the Outside World* London, Tavistock Publications Ltd 1959.

> The work of Dr. Bowlby and Dr. Winnicott is of outstanding importance to all who are concerned with the problems of children.

THE END